THE SIGNIFICANCE OF NITROGEN

Modern synthetic ammonia plant at Belle, W. Va.

The Significance of Nitrogen

by

J. ENRIQUE ZANETTI
Professor of Chemistry, Columbia University

with an introduction by

FRANCIS P. GARVAN
President of The Chemical Foundation, Incorporated

6940

THE CHEMICAL FOUNDATION, INCORPORATED
654 Madison Avenue
New York

Published, 1932, by

THE CHEMICAL FOUNDATION, INC.

Printed in the United States of America

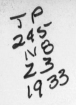

INTRODUCTION

Last week, in Germany, an agreement was signed of the utmost importance to the people of the United States.

It was an agreement controlling production and sale of natural and synthetic nitrogen and was signed by the nitrogen companies of every country in Europe and by Cosach, the Chilean nitrate monopoly.

So secret were the proceedings that only one copy was signed by the different companies involved and then only with initials, and this secret copy was deposited in a safe deposit box in Germany, each of the signing companies being handed a carbon copy of this agreement without any signatures attached.

This agreement, known as the International Nitrogen Cartel, can only be successful through the destruction of the nitrogen industry of the United States.

This concert followed a general concert of the chemical companies of Europe in the International Dye Cartel and is almost simultaneous with the foreign debt concert which has now demanded the cancellation of its debts to this country.

Lonely America is right!

Modern national defense is based on the airplane industry, plus the chemical industry—the gun and the load.

The American chemical industry, from the small beginnings of 1914, has been built up by the American people— its schools and colleges, its Congress and its business men —until it stands ready to provide for our national defense, our national health and our national agriculture and industry.

The world is combining to destroy it!

In this endeavor, foreign nations are being assisted by the misuse of American depositors' money, under the control of our so-called international bankers.

Over one hundred millions of American savings have been sunk in aiding these hostile competitors now banded against us. This amount we know, as it is covered by public offerings. How much more, in secret or short term loans, we do not know.

It has become the duty of The Chemical Foundation to place the facts before the American people, and in discharging its duty, it has borne the expense of an exhaustive investigation by Professor J. Enrique Zanetti, Professor of Chemistry at Columbia University, and Colonel in the Chemical Warfare Reserves, U. S. Army, and now to place his conclusions before you. It is up to you.

We particularly bespeak your attention to Chapters IV and V.

FRANCIS P. GARVAN,
President of The Chemical Foundation,
Incorporated.

December 1st, 1932.

PREFACE

This little volume is not intended for chemists, engineers or the technically trained in general. To them is opened the vast store of the professional publications specially written in their own language. But the average reader, who does not possess the sesame that will open the storehouse of scientific literature, is entitled to be enlightened on a topic that has of late become of increasing importance. Hardly a day passes without mention in the daily press of the formation of "nitrogen cartels", of the struggle between the "synthetic nitrogen producers" among themselves and the whole field against "the Chilean producers", of the reorganization of "the Cosach" with its immense capitalization, Congressional discussions of the "Muscle Shoals fertilizer plant", "dumping of sulphate" in our markets, the indirect effects of "low nitrate prices" on the Chilean revolution and many others which it would take too long to enumerate. What is it all about? To be sure every one knows more or less that these nitrogen matters have some bearing on fertilizers but the equally significant bearing on national defense and the chemical industry is not so widely recognized though of quite as vital an importance.

It is with the object of reaching the non-technical reader, whose influence will be paramount in the solution of some of the problems arising out of the struggle that is now being waged in the field of nitrogen, that this little volume has been written. Technical terms have been avoided as far as possible and not one chemical reaction is to be found in its pages.

The first chapter deals with nitrogen in general and the second with the Chilean nitrate industry. There is little strictly technical matter in these, but the third chapter has necessarily to be more so as its subject—The Atmospheric Nitrogen Industry—can hardly be treated otherwise. Every endeavor, however, has been made to describe the various processes as simply as possible.   The fourth chapter deals historically with the development of the nitrogen industry in the United States and the fifth records conclusions as to the probable future of the struggle between the natural and synthetic nitrogen products.

The writer begs to express his appreciation to his colleague Professor Hal T. Beans, of Columbia University, and to Mr. P. E. Howard, of the Fixed Nitrogen Research Laboratory, Department of Agriculture, for many valuable suggestions.

Technical books on this subject have been freely drawn upon.   Special acknowledgment is due to *Fixed Nitrogen* by Harry A. Curtis, *The Fixation of Atmospheric Nitrogen* by F. A. Ernst, *Nitric Acid and Nitrates*, by A. G. Cottrell, numerous publications of Government Bureaus, and articles in *Industrial and Engineering Chemistry, Chemical & Metallurgical Engineering, The Fertilizer Review*, and *Fortune*.

The object of the book has been not originality but interpretation.   It is intended as an educational rather than a technical contribution.

J. E. Z.

Columbia University,
New York City, December 1st, 1932.

CONTENTS

APPENDIX

ILLUSTRATIONS

CHAPTER I

NITROGEN IN GENERAL

HISTORICAL

Nitrogen is one of the members of the family of 92 elements which make up our universe. Its presence has been detected in remote stars and nebulae and in the sun. In some stars it is present in the form of cyanogen, a compound it forms with carbon, very stable at the high temperatures prevailing in those stars, and it has even been shown to exist in the tails of comets. On the earth it occurs chiefly in the form of the free element, a tasteless, odorless gas showing little chemical activity and forming 79 per cent of the atmosphere.

The recognition of the elementary nature of nitrogen dates only from 1772 when an English chemist, Rutherford, showed that when oxygen was removed from the air, there was left a gas which did not support combustion. Priestley and Cavendish, two of Rutherford's countrymen, in the chemical parlance of the day, named it "dephlogisticated air".

While the ancients were not acquainted with nitrogen as an element they knew several of its compounds. One of the earliest known was saltpetre or niter. Saltpetre, the scientific name of which is potassium nitrate, was known in India from very early times. A special sect, the Shorawallá, made it their business to manufacture and sell this salt which they obtained by mixing wood ashes with the surface soil from the neighborhood of stables, manure piles and drain pipes. This soil usually contained considerable amounts of nitrates, chiefly calcium and potassium nitrates, formed by the action of bacteria on decaying organic matter. They treated this mixture with water which dissolved out the saltpetre and after evaporation, crystals of impure saltpetre were obtained. It was also obtained by the washing of certain porous rocks rich in potassium, where it had formed from the same bacterial action, hence the name *sal petrae* by which the ancient alchemists designated it. The Chinese were also acquainted with saltpetre and still manufacture it by the same age old method of piling up manure and refuse, adding lime and wood ashes and allowing the pile to stand for a year or so when they wash it with water which extracts the saltpetre. From the thirteenth century to the last quarter of the nineteenth saltpetre was chiefly used as a component of gunpowder and fireworks and was imported into Europe from India.

The alchemists were also familiar with other compounds of nitrogen such as ammonium chloride, which they called "sal-ammoniac", and with ammonia, a compound of nitrogen and hydrogen, gaseous at ordinary temperatures and very soluble in water. This was obtained by heating leather or horn or urine with lime and absorbing the gas that was given off in water. Until not so very long ago solutions of ammonia in water were known to pharmacists as "spirits of hartshorn".

The names "ammonia" and "ammonium" are incorrectly derived from the temple of Jupiter Ammon, near the ruins of which, in the Lybian desert, salt-like deposits were found which the alchemists thought to be identical with "sal-ammoniac", but were, as a matter of fact, entirely different chemically. The confusion is said to have arisen from the original name of true sal-ammoniac, which was made in the East from the distillation of camel's dung and imported into Europe under the name of *sal-armoniacum*. Nitric acid, which was called "spiritus fumans glauberi", and later "aqua fortis", was also known to the alchemists.

OCCURRENCE

Nitrogen forms a great many compounds with other elements, but these are characterized by their instability, their tendency to break up, and consequently we find that the amount of nitrogen compounds existing in the earth's crust is so small that its percentage, when compared with that of other elements like oxygen, silicon and iron, is minute and considered negligible.

The amount of nitrogen contained in the soil has been estimated at 40 billion tons,* to which must be added another 100 billion tons contained in coal and peat. This is, however, a very small amount compared with the total weight of the earth of 6,600 billion billion tons, about 50 per cent of which consists of the element oxygen. The atmosphere is a richer source of nitrogen, for, on every square mile of the earth's surface rest 22,000,000 tons of nitrogen, making the total amount nearly 4 million billion tons.

NITROGEN AND LIFE

It is one of the strange mysteries of nature that this element, unstable in its compounds and found chiefly in its uncombined state, should be one of the most important in the various processes associated with life. For, the chief products which constitute the elementary protoplasm and the bodily tissues, are compounds of nitrogen. Their instability, their continuous breaking up, call for constant renewal of the nitrogen supply in some form suitable to the delicate chemical reactions that maintain life. Other elements are also necessary to life, but all these are found in nature in the form of perfectly stable compounds; the nitrogen derivatives, however, are essentially unstable.

The amount of nitrogen existing in plant and animal tissue has been estimated as follows:

Forests . . . . 592 million tons
Animals . . . . . . 9 million tons
Human population . . . 2 million tons

Animals and most plants are entirely incapable of supplying the nitrogen needed by their tissues from the free nitrogen of the air. Only certain bacteria, algae and fungi are able to do this. These bacteria "fix" the free nitrogen and change it to compounds that can be absorbed by the plant

---

*The ton used in this book is the short ton of 2,000 pounds, unless otherwise stated.

and used by it to build up tissue. The importance of this bacterial action is paramount for the maintenance of life on the earth. Occurring in all fertile soils, working sometimes independently, sometimes in association with certain plants, these bacteria make available some of the vast nitrogen supply of the atmosphere to the plants, from which in turn animals supply their needs. It is estimated that from bacterial action the soil receives some 20 pounds of nitrogen per acre every year. If, however, the soil bacteria are able to work in association with certain plants belonging to the family of the *leguminosae*, like peas, beans, clover, lucerne (alfalfa), and many others, the amount of nitrogen made available increases to an average of some 60 pounds per acre, and may in some cases be as high as 160 pounds. The roots of these plants act as hosts to the bacteria which penetrate them causing little swellings or nodules to form in which billions of the bacteria live and multiply, assimilating free nitrogen and changing it to ammonia or nitrates which the plant can utilize. About two-thirds of the nitrogen assimilated by such plants comes directly from the air. The balance comes from the accumulated soil reserve or artificial fertilization. A 3-ton crop of cow peas, for example, will take 86 pounds of nitrogen from the air, a 4-ton crop of clover 106 pounds, and a 4-ton alfalfa crop 132 pounds.

That these plants with the help of bacteria are able to assimilate nitrogen directly from the air has been shown to be the case by growing them in nitrogen free sand after inoculating their roots with nitrogen fixing bacteria and adding to the sand only the other mineral salts necessary to plant growth.

The bacteria and the leguminous plants are not the only source by which nature makes nitrogen available to sustain life. The flash of lightning in a thunderstorm, passing through the air and heating it to incandescence along its path, causes some of the nitrogen to unite with oxygen forming gaseous oxides of nitrogen which being washed down by rain into the soil, and combining with some of the soil constituents such as lime, form nitrates, and these can be utilized by plant life. This source, however, is a distinctly minor one. In particular localities where thunderstorms are frequent as much as six pounds of nitrogen per acre can be made available every year, but the average is certainly not higher than one pound per acre.

From the simpler compounds of nitrogen, the plant builds up extremely complex ones, the proteins, which are the only sources of nitrogen available to animal life. The animal body is not only unable to assimilate nitrogen directly from the free element, but cannot even utilize its simpler compounds as the plant does. Animal life is then entirely dependent for sustenance either on plant tissues or on the tissues of other animals that have previously fed on the plants.

Extensive experiments have been carried out for the purpose of synthesizing in the laboratory these very complex nitrogen compounds that are built up by the plants or the animals that feed on them, these proteins, so as to make them directly available to man as food, but these experiments have not yet succeeded in duplicating any but the simplest ones and have so far proved far too costly to be considered as even a remote possibility in the solution of the food problem of mankind. The plant still holds its secret.

THE NITROGEN CYCLE

As animal and plant tissues die and decay, nitrogen is set free again from the proteins either in the uncombined condition or in the form of one of its simpler compounds, ammonia, which, as stated above, is a compound of hydrogen and nitrogen. Another type of bacteria from the one which helped to "fix" nitrogen, the *de-nitrifying bacteria*, go to work on the dead tissue and liberate free nitrogen and ammonia. The ammonia liberated is washed down again into the soil by rain and taken up once more by plants or changed by other bacteria to nitrates, but the liberated free nitrogen must remain in the air until the above mentioned agencies, and others devised by man, will take it up again and "fix" it to be available to plant life.

Nitrogen then follows a complete cycle:

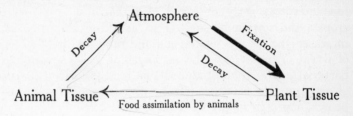

The nitrogen cycle is represented here only in its main aspect. As stated, ammonia is one of the products of putrefaction and as it is not decomposed easily into its elements it is either taken up by some plants directly or changed to nitrates by the soil bacteria. There is, therefore, another inner cycle within that given in which part of the nitrogen keeps circulating from living to dead tissue and back again to living tissue through plant absorption until it may be liberated by decomposition of proteins and the action of de-nitrifying bacteria.

ORGANIC NITROGENOUS FERTILIZERS

Since the growing of crops is dependent on the available nitrogen supply, the yields will be limited by the amount of nitrogen that bacteria can provide. However, if the nitrogen supply is artificially increased, the yield per acre will increase also, other things being equal. This fact has been known from very early times though not correctly explained until about 1840.

At that time the scientific study of plant food requirements were initiated by the great German chemist, von Liebig, and since then the matter has received increasing attention from investigators. A branch of chemistry, agricultural chemistry, is entirely devoted to it and one of the great industries of the world, the fertilizer industry, is concerned with the production of the necessary additional plant food.

Until the third decade of the past century the only available forms of "fixed" nitrogen were manure and farm refuse.

These products of animal and vegetable decay, setting free simpler nitrogenous compounds, formed an excellent plant food. It was early observed also that the "rotation of crops", the sowing of such crops as clover, lucerne, etc., increased the fertility of the soil and produced better crops of wheat or barley, long before anything was known of the bacterial action that produced this increase. But the use of manures and the other natural agencies would at present be insufficient to supply the food requirements of the present world population especially since farm animals, one of the chief sources of manure, have been so crowded out in this machine age.

Besides manure, other sources of nitrogen became available as science progressed and plant requirements were studied and more clearly understood. Fish scrap, leather scrap, cottonseed meal, guano (excrements of sea birds), refuse and dried blood from the slaughter houses and many other sources of nitrogen, so-called "organic" because they were the direct waste product of animal or vegetable life, were and still are extensively used.

INORGANIC NITROGENOUS FERTILIZERS

Another type of fertilizer, the inorganic, so called because they have no connection with decaying organic matter came into general use beginning about 1840. These fertilizers consist of mineral or artificially made products, nitrates, salts of ammonia and other nitrogen compounds which, though entirely unrelated to life, can be used by the plants as food.

The success of these fertilizers in the markets of the world was not won without a struggle. The farmers, an essentially conservative class everywhere, were very dubious of the efficiency of these clean looking, generally odorless products quite different from the manures and organic fertilizers to which they had been accustomed. Even at the present time some fertilizer manufacturers mix into their products some malodorous fish scrap or decomposing slaughter house refuse chiefly to cater to this prejudice which, however, has almost entirely died out.

In 1809 it was discovered that a substance found in large quantities in the soils of the desert areas of Chile and Peru, "Chile saltpetre", or more scientifically, sodium nitrate, could be used as a source of nitrogen for plants and from that time on, beginning with a modest shipment of some hundred tons in 1831 and reaching a peak of 3,300,000 tons in 1918, "Chile saltpetre" has been, until recent years, one of the chief sources of fertilizer nitrogen in the world. A special chapter is devoted to the Chilean nitrate industry to which the reader is referred for further details.

Another important source of nitrogen compounds was found in the products of the distillation of coal to make illuminating gas. Coal, being derived from the accumulation of vegetable debris many millions of years ago in the Carboniferous Era, still retains small amounts of nitrogen compounds (1 - 2% by weight). When the coal is heated to make gas, these compounds are broken down forming chiefly ammonia which passes off with the gas.

Ammonia is very soluble in water whereas the remainder of the illuminating gas is not, so that if the gas as it comes from coal is bubbled through water, most of the ammonia dissolves in the water and the balance of the gas passes on. This solution of ammonia in water, called "ammonia liquor", was until twenty-five years ago the only available large scale source of ammonia compounds.

A more efficient method of removing the ammonia consists in bubbling the coal gas through a dilute solution of sulphuric acid in water. From this solution ammonium sulphate separates out in a crystalline form, somewhat resembling brown sugar. This ammonium sulphate, after drying, is bagged and sold as fertilizer material.

It seems a long way from the inorganic nitrogen industry to the steel industry, and yet the two are closely connected. The steel industry requires enormous quantities of coke and coke is obtained by heating coal in large ovens or retorts. Under those conditions, as in the making of illuminating gas,

Fig. 1.—"Beehive" coke ovens with some of their product in foreground.

Courtesy of *The Fertilizer Review.*

Fig. 2—Modern by-product coke oven.

the volatile products of the coal—tar and gas—are given off and there remains behind a hard porous mass, the coke, constituting about 70% of the original weight of the coal.

Formerly coke was made by heating coal in large brick ovens called "beehive" ovens because of their shape (Fig. 1). A vent at the top allowed the volatile products to pass off and these were ignited and allowed to burn in the air. When the flame at the vent died down, the coke maker knew there were no more volatile products to be given off and the coal had been changed to coke.

The chemist soon showed, however, that the tar that was produced from heating the coal was a rich source of basic compounds which could be utilized for the manufacture of dyes, medicines, and countless industrial products and that the gas could be partly used to heat the coal and result in a saving of fuel. It became then highly profitable to build special ovens, called "by-product coke ovens", to effect these savings (Fig. 2). More coal gas then became available and consequently more ammonia also.

The ammonia from this source is marketed as ammonium sulphate and known to the trade as "by-product ammonium sulphate". The industry has made enormous progress in the last fifty years and has reached an annual capacity of 2,250,000 tons of sulphate.

Ammonium sulphate is an excellent nitrogenous fertilizer. The only objection that has been brought against it is that the soil bacteria utilize the ammonia but leave the sulphuric acid. This tends to make the soil acid—"sour" as the farmers say—but an occasional application of lime corrects this drawback at little expense.

It is difficult to estimate the actual cost of producing ammonium sulphate. As it is not manufactured for its own sake but is merely a by-product of the coke industry, the bookkeeping method of apportioning costs over the many other by-products enters largely into its total cost. The chief items are, of course, the price of the sulphuric acid, labor, bagging and amortization of the special machinery used in its production and separation, but what fraction of the cost of the coal, amortization of capital invested in the ovens, etc., should be applied to the ammonium sulphate, is the item that varies with the bookkeeping method employed.

Of late years, increased competition from the synthetic ammonia industry has lowered the price of the "by-product ammonium sulphate" to about one-third its pre-war price and it can be obtained at present (1932) for about $18.00 a ton. This, too, in spite of a diminished supply, for as the coke industry is dependent on the steel industry, and the latter is now operating at about 20 per cent capacity, the coke industry is also depressed and less ammonia is available from that source.

Ammonium sulphate contains 21.2 per cent of nitrogen when in the pure condition. The commercial product, however, usually contains about 20 per cent owing to impurities which it is not necessary to remove before marketing.

INDUSTRIAL USES OF NITROGEN

So far we have considered only the utilization of nitrogen compounds in connection with food. There are, however, many other important uses of nitrogen.

One of the chief of these is for the manufacture of explosives. As the compounds of nitrogen are essentially unstable they are particularly adaptable for use as explosives. An explosive is required to set free rapidly the energy which was stored up in its molecules while it was being manufactured, and compounds of nitrogen are specially suited to this purpose.

Nearly all high explosives are nitrogen compounds. Dynamite, TNT and picric acid are familiar names to every one. They are all nitrogen compounds, as are also the smokeless powders that came into general use during the last quarter of the past century. For their manufacture large quantities of nitric acid are used every year.

One must not consider the explosive industry as purely a war industry. Explosives have their peace uses as well, for blasting in building or mining operations. Such outstanding human achievements as the Panama Canal would have been all but impossible without the use of high explosives.

Large quantities of nitric acid are used in the dye industry and also in the manufacture of plastic materials such as celluloid and pyroxylin, widely used for photographic films.

As these chemical industries developed and the food requirements of the world increased, the demand for new and cheaper sources of nitrogen increased also, so that it soon became apparent that we must tap the practically inexhaustible supply of nitrogen from the atmosphere. Then the chemist went to work.

THE FIXATION OF ATMOSPHERIC NITROGEN

The story of the development of the fixation of atmospheric nitrogen is one of the most fascinating chapters in the history of science.

At the beginning of this century there was a general belief, later shown to have been quite erroneous, that humanity was facing a crisis in its nitrogen problem. The Chilean nitrate beds, the chief source of nitrogen at the time, were thought to be approaching exhaustion and since ammonia could be obtained from coal only by coking it, one could not expect the coke industry to go on increasing its output of ammonia indefinitely unless it could market its coke. As the demand was increasing every year, the point seemed to that generation not far off when a shortage would be felt and agricultural production suffer accordingly. The dependence of the nations of the world on the far off Chilean deposits appeared also as strategically dangerous in case of a blockade. All these factors combined intensified the search for a method to manufacture nitrogen compounds from the readily available unlimited raw material in the atmosphere. In less than fifteen years, the chemical industry solved the problem and can now supply the entire world requirement if called upon to do so from atmospheric nitrogen. It is furthermore capable of practically unlimited expansion. For whatever amount of nitrogen is withdrawn from the atmosphere by "fixation" is ultimately returned to

it by the nitrogen cycle and even though the present requirements be multiplied yearly for generations to come, they
will diminish the atmospheric stock but infinitesimally and
that only for a while. We cannot really "fix" nitrogen, we
can only borrow and use it temporarily. Ultimately it finds
its own way back to freedom.

The fixation of nitrogen on an industrial scale is carried
out by three main processes. The first, which was developed
chiefly at the beginning of this century, fixed nitrogen by
one of nature's methods, the lightning flash. Air was passed
through an electric arc and the oxides of nitrogen thus
formed, all of them gases at ordinary temperatures, were
absorbed in water and then treated with lime to form
calcium nitrate. This process is now little used.

The second process developed consisted in passing nitrogen
over calcium carbide, a compound widely used to make
acetylene gas, at an elevated temperature. Under those
conditions the nitrogen enters into combination with the
calcium carbide forming calcium cyanamide and free carbon.
There is only a technical name to designate this compound
but it has been talked about so much that the word cyanamide
is no longer a total stranger. Cyanamide can be used directly
as a fertilizer for when treated with water, it slowly forms
ammonia which can be utilized by the soil bacteria and the
plants. Calcium cyanamide should contain theoretically
35 per cent of nitrogen, but the commercial product contains
only about 20 per cent. The world capacity for its manufacture amounts to about 2,100,000 tons a year. This
means that about 400,000 tons of nitrogen can be fixed
yearly by that process.

By far, however, the most important process for the
fixation of nitrogen is the one that brings about the combination of nitrogen with hydrogen to form ammonia gas.
The advantage of this process is chiefly its flexibility. Not
only is ammonia—its direct product—of great commercial
value but it can be changed into a large number of other
products. For example, the ammonia can be converted to
ammonium sulphate or it can be caused to combine with

oxygen and form nitric acid which is not only a valuable product in itself, but will give us other important products such as sodium nitrate, formerly obtained only from Chile, or ammonium nitrate. Since nitric acid is the basis of the explosive industry, such a process becomes an essential part of every system of national defense while at the same time furnishing the much needed fertilizer material. These considerations have placed this process far ahead of all the others. Its capacity has increased by leaps and bounds in the last ten years so that it has now reached over 2,200,000 tons of nitrogen annually. This means that if all the ammonia produced were changed to ammonium sulphate, it would produce 10,000,000 tons of ammonium sulphate, or four times the annual capacity of the by-product coke ovens. If changed to sodium nitrate it would mean an annual production of 14,000,000 tons of sodium nitrate or six times the average Chilean nitrate production. Of course, what determines the final disposal of the ammonia will be the market conditions. It cannot be either all changed to sodium nitrate, to ammonium sulphate nor to nitric acid and it must be borne in mind also that capacity does not mean production, for under present conditions of industrial and agricultural depression actual production is but a fraction of the annual capacity.

We can at any rate feel certain now that humanity is far from being faced with a nitrogen famine. The capacity of the by-product coke ovens, the cyanamide process and the ammonia process and one or two other minor ones is now well over 3,300,000 tons of fixed nitrogen a year, or more than enough to take care of the probable world consumption for some time to come.

With the bugbear of the exhaustion of the practical sources of nitrogen out of the way, the chemist's concern now is to make the available nitrogen cheaper and cheaper. Knowing that certain bacteria can in some way "fix" atmospheric nitrogen, he is now interested in finding out how these lowly little brethren of ours, far down in the scale of life, can do it. Could he, the chemist, helped by the bacteriologist use them to fix nitrogen for mankind on an industrial scale or could they teach him a better way than the one he now uses? These questions are now being seriously asked in the laboratory. What the answer will be, no one knows. Industrial processes based on bacterial action are, of course, very old. The fermentation industries have used them for generations, but lately compounds which one never thought thirty years ago could be made profitably by bacterial action, such as acetone and butyl alcohol, valuable industrial solvents, are now manufactured on a large scale by bacteria. Whether the cheaper sources will be found by lowering present production costs or whether a new path must be blazed remains to be decided by scientific research.

OTHER PLANT FOODS

Plants require some forty-two of the eighty-nine known elements to develop properly. Of these, however, all but three are found in sufficient amounts in practically all soils. This trilogy—nitrogen, phosphorus and potassium—forms the base on which is built the fertilizer industry. They are all three necessary and deficiency of any one of them will interfere with proper plant development. It was, for example, a common belief among European farmers about 1860–70 that the use of Chile saltpetre as a fertilizer "exhausted" the soil. The observation was correct, for the stimulation of plant growth by the Chile saltpetre caused the plant to draw more heavily on the stores of phosphates and potassium salts of the soil and if these were not replenished, the plant growth was checked. As soon, however, as it became understood that these other elements were equally necessary and "mixed" fertilizer containing potash and phosphate came into general use, the prejudice died out.

FERTILIZER NITROGEN

It is not possible in this little volume to dwell on the fertilizer question except in what concerns nitrogen directly. For plant food purposes the content of nitrogen in a fertilizer is the chief concern. Whether the nitrogen is supplied in the form of ammonium salts which the soil bacteria convert to nitrates readily or directly in the form of nitrate such as Chile saltpetre or ammonium nitrate, the nitrogen content is the important matter. For that reason the federal and state laws require that the nitrogen content along with the potash and phosphate be clearly indicated on the label of the fertilizer sold.

Again it is essential that the nitrogen be in a form which either the soil bacteria can convert to an assimilable form or the plant can take up directly into its tissues. Some nitrogen compounds, for example potassium cyanide, would be fatal to plant life. In general, salts of ammonium, nitrates and others like cyanamide and urea that will be readily decomposed to ammonia are the chief forms in which nitrogen is now used in fertilizers. Of late years such fertilizers as tankage from slaughter houses and cottonseed meal have found other uses as stock foods and the cost of nitrogen supplied in this form is too high for general use.

Table I gives the nitrogen contents of the chief nitrogenous fertilizers.

TABLE I.

Average Fixed Nitrogen Content of Fertilizer Materials.

Organic	Per cent	Inorganic	Per cent
Cottonseed meal	6– 8	*Ammonium sulphate	21.2
Fish scrap	7–12	*Sodium nitrate	16.5
Dried blood	10–16	*Ammonium nitrate	35.
Leather scrap	6–15	Calcium cyanamide	20.
Guano	0–10	*Potassium nitrate	13.8
Manure	0– 1	*Calcium nitrate	17.
Bone meal	3– 5		

Statistics of production and consumption of nitrogen compounds are usually given in tons of nitrogen. In this country the short ton or "net ton" of 2000 lbs. is generally employed but abroad the metric ton of 2204 lbs. is used. From the nitrogen tonnage the production of the particular compound

*Content of nitrogen in the pure compound. The commercial product has sensibly less.

can be readily figured. For example, when one reads that the world production of ammonium sulphate in 1930–31 was "390,000 net tons of nitrogen" it means that since every ton of ammonium sulphate contains only about 20 per cent nitrogen or $\frac{1}{5}$ of its weight (allowing for impurities that are generally present) the total production of ammonium sulphate was five times the figure given or 1,950,000 tons of sulphate. When the production of Chilean nitrate is given as "275,000 net tons of nitrogen", since Chile saltpetre contains about 16 per cent of nitrogen, or roughly one sixth of its weight, the amount of nitrate is six times that figure or approximately 1,650,000 tons of Chilean nitrate.*

Now that we have had a general view of the field, let us turn to the more detailed discussion of the important sources of nitrogen.

*The actual factors usually employed to convert nitrogen tonnage are 4.8 for ammonium sulphate and 6.4 for Chilean nitrate.

CHAPTER II

THE CHILEAN NITRATE INDUSTRY

GENERAL AND HISTORICAL

The traveler who sails down the coast of Peru and Chile cannot help being impressed by the forbidding barrenness of the seacoast. From the moment he leaves the port of Callao and for some fifteen hundred miles south, not a trace of vegetation, not a blade of grass, not even a cactus growth can be discerned growing on the hills of the coastal range. Should he land at one of the dusty seaports and venture a few miles inland, he would be confronted by one of the most desolate sights on earth, the Pampa, the desert plateau lying between the coast hills and the majestic Andes. This long strip of desert stretching from southern Peru to central Chile, and varying from one hundred to one hundred and fifty miles in width, is uniformly covered with a dirty brown earth, and dotted over its surface with innumerable rock fragments varying in size from pebbles to fairly large boulders. Rain very rarely falls. A generation of the tenacious population that clings to the seacoast may be born and grow to manhood and never in that time know what rain is. One single river, the Loa, reaches the coast from the mountains, but its water is so brackish as to be unfit for use. The wealthier towns can afford to bring their water supply from the Andes by pipe lines laid across the desert, but the smaller and poorer ones cannot pay for such luxury. They obtain their water supply from the distillation of seawater. All food, except fish, and all fuel must be imported. One does not wonder then that the Spanish conquistadores and viceroys left that entire strip of seacoast severely alone, for of what possible use could it be in assuaging their thirst for gold or supplying their home government with the excise

17

taxes that they levied upon the rich agricultural lands and
the famous mines of Peru? And yet, they would turn over in
their graves could they but know the wealth that lay con-
cealed in the desert, could they but realize that the Chilean
government, in export taxes alone, has received in fifty
years over $900,000,000 from a desert product, *salitre*, the
Chile saltpetre, that lies imbedded but a few feet under
the surface.

It was not till 1809 that a German resident of Bolivia
called attention to the fact that the so-called Chile saltpetre that had been extracted in a more or less desultory
fashion since the middle of the 18th century was an excellent
fertilizer. Very little was done about this discovery for
more than twenty years. The exploitation was extremely
crude, and only the richest ores were worked, but gradually
the value of this new fertilizer began to be realized and
exports to England began in 1831, the first shipment consisting of 110 tons, and being sold at $108 a ton. The ex-
ports slowly grew, reaching 8,600 tons in 1840 with the
price being lowered to $80 a ton. Most of this nitrate was
used for agricultural purposes. By 1860 the industry had
increased to sizable proportions with an exportation of
56,000 tons.

This nitrate, though called Chile saltpetre, was in reality
found in the deserts of southern Peru and Bolivia. In 1879,
however, war broke out between those two countries and
Chile, and when peace was signed two years later the Tarapacá Desert, as this region is called, became Chilean terri-
tory. The value of the nitrate in this desert constituted
the heaviest war indemnity that any nation had paid up
to that time. Immense wealth passed into the hands of the
Chileans. Huge fortunes have been made out of the exploitation of these deposits, and since 1882 until recent years
the Government has derived a large share of its revenue
from a tax of $12 levied on every metric ton of nitrate
exported. As years passed the industry grew almost unin-
terruptedly, reaching a peak during the World War in 1918,
when 3,300,000 tons were exported. For Chile saltpetre is

not only utilized by agriculture, but also for the making of nitric acid and nitric acid is the base on which rests the entire explosive and smokeless powder industry. Hundreds of millions of dollars were collected by the Chileans during the War from the sale of their nitrates which had jumped under the pressing demands of the war industries from $50 a ton to $150 a ton. And they could have asked any price, for the Allies were completely dependent on them. Nowhere else in the world are deposits of sodium nitrate found in sufficient amounts for industrial exploitation. No more complete natural monopoly could have been imagined.

The outbreak of the War had found the Allies without any important source of nitric acid but those unique deposits eight thousand miles away. Strategically they were at a disadvantage. Admiral von Spee, commanding the German squadron in Asiatic waters, understood this situation fully and after detaching the famous Emden on her adventurous career, made all possible haste across the Pacific to the Chilean coast to stop the shipments of nitrate to his enemies. His arrival at Valparaiso caused consternation among the Allies. Nitrate shipments, urgently needed in England and France for munitions, stopped and prices of stocks in private hands began to climb rapidly. The situation was further aggravated when a British squadron under command of Admiral Craddock was defeated by the Germans off the Chilean town of Coronel. The German guns outranged the British, and the latter lost all their ships but one. The British had to despatch two of their most powerful cruisers from the home fleet to deal with von Spee's squadron. These cruisers had just arrived at the Falkland Islands and were coaling when von Spee, driven from the Pacific by the approach of the Japanese fleet, met them and this time the situation was reversed, for the British had gun superiority and in the ensuing battle sank all but two of von Spee's smaller and unimportant cruisers.

The general public little realized the importance of those two naval actions and looked upon them as mere encounters between opposing squadrons. But the matter was of far deeper import. Von Spee had touched a vital spot and not until he was disposed of did the Allies breathe easier. The memory of those anxious months, intensified later by Germany's submarine campaign, has been a lasting one; a bitter lesson was learned and the doom of Chilean monopoly was sealed. Never again would a nation fighting for its existence, unless grossly negligent, find itself cut off from its base of ammunition and fertilizer supply thousands of miles away. The chemist would see to that.

THE NITRATE DEPOSITS

But let us return to the nitrate deposits themselves. These do not occur uniformly distributed over the entire desert but in definite areas or fields. Their extent is enormous and every estimate that has been made has had to be increased within a few years by the discovery of new fields. In 1898, Sir William Crookes, in a presidential address to the British Association for the Advancement of Science, estimated that the deposits would be exhausted by 1931, but in 1921 the amount of nitrate in sight was placed at 250,000,-000 tons, or enough to last one hundred years more and there are still vast desert areas which have not been explored.

The nitrate is found in the fields in a rather uniform manner. It occurs in a layer from one to four feet under the surface, rarely deeper. The layer itself varies in thickness. There may be pockets ten or twelve feet thick and in places it thins out to a foot or so but the average thickness is four feet. The ground above and below contains very little nitrate. The nitrate bearing layer is locally known as *caliche*, the upper layer of earth and minerals, poor in nitrate, as *costra* and *chuca* and the sodium nitrate when extracted as *salitre*.

How these deposits were formed remains a mystery. Many theories have been advanced but none has proved satisfactory. It has been proposed that they are the remains of extensive guano deposits from the innumerable sea birds that have lived for ages on this coast, but the fact that no phosphates are found in these deposits, as there surely

would be if that were their origin, makes that theory un-
tenable. Again it was postulated that they were formed in
a long past geologic era from the decay of marine vegetable
matter of a vast inland sea that subsequently dried up, but
the fact that the element bromine which is found in all seawater is entirely absent in the caliche caused the abandonment of that theory. Volcanic action, at one time intensive
along this coast, has also been called upon to explain these
deposits. Ammonium salts are not infrequently found in the
neighborhood of volcanoes and these salts may have inter-
acted with the oxygen of the air to form nitrates. Again it
has been proposed that in ages past this region was subject
to intense electrical storms that caused oxides of nitrogen
to form in the air and these being washed down by rain
formed nitrates by interaction with the soil constituents.
But flaws either chemical or geological can be picked in all
these theories and in the end we must admit our ignorance
of just how the nitrate deposits were formed and why they
occur as they do in fields and so uniformly distributed in
those fields.

The composition of the caliche varies somewhat from field
to field. The amount of sodium nitrate ranges from 8 to
30 per cent. Hand picked specimens may contain as much
as 60 per cent but the general average composition is as
follows:

	Per cent
Sodium nitrate .	20.
*Potassium nitrate .	minute
Sodium chloride (common salt) .	20.13
Sodium sulphate (Glauber's salt) .	2.8
Calcium sulphate (gypsum) .	6.3
Magnesium sulphate (Epsom salts) .	4.05
Sodium iodate .	.15
Insolubles (clay, sand, etc.) .	45.5
Undetermined (borates, perchlorates, etc.)	1.

*Some samples of caliche may contain as high as 17 per cent potassium nitrate but
the general run contains very little.

Of the constituents of the caliche only two are of value, the sodium nitrate and the sodium iodate. In some fields the borate content ran high enough to be used as a source of borax some years ago but cheaper sources in California have eliminated this industry in Chile. The problem of exploitation consists chiefly in extracting the nitrate without having it contaminated by the other substances present, especially the sodium chloride, which would decrease its value as a fertilizer as well as a source of nitric acid.

PRINCIPLES OF THE NITRATE SEPARATION

In separating the constituents advantage is taken of the fact that substances vary not only in their solubility in cold water but as the temperature of the water is increased, the solubilities vary again, generally increasing though not in the same proportion. Sodium nitrate for example is much more soluble in hot water than it is in cold but sodium chloride (common salt) is only little more soluble in hot water than it is in cold water. If a mixture, then, of sodium nitrate and of sodium chloride, such as occurs in caliche, is heated with water until no more will dissolve—the chemist says, "until the solution is saturated"—both will go into solution but much more of the nitrate than of the chloride, a good deal of which will be left behind as a solid. If the hot solution poured off from the chloride is then cooled much nitrate will separate out but very little chloride. The nitrate is said to *crystallize* out. If the crystals of nitrate are then separated by pouring off the solution or straining them through a fine sieve, there will be but little chloride mixed with them, and if the process be repeated, there would be practically no chloride left and pure sodium nitrate would be obtained. This is in brief the principle of the method employed by the processes for extracting nitrate from caliche.

THE SHANKS PROCESS

In getting at the caliche the upper layer or costra must first be removed or loosened. This is done by blasting it off with powder charges laid in the soil at intervals and varying

Courtesy of Chemical & Metallurgical Engineering.

Fig. 3—A Shanks process plant in the Chilean desert.

From Cottrell's Nitric Acid and Nitrates.

Fig. 4—The old hand method of mining caliche.

Fig. 5—Shanks process crystallizing tanks.

Fig. 6—Removing nitrate from crystallizing tanks. [Shanks process.

in power with the depth of the costra. The costra is then scraped off and the caliche itself loosened by another blasting operation or by hand tools. Workmen are then able to pick out the larger fragments and load them into horse-carts and temporary narrow gauge railway cars to convey them to the extraction plant locally known as the "oficina".

The first operation at the plant consists in crushing the caliche to small pieces about 1–1½ inches and sifting out the dust and smaller particles, the "fines", as they are technically known. The crushed caliche is then dumped into large iron tanks and covered with water. The water is heated by means of steam coils to near the boiling point. The soluble constituents, the nitrate, some of the common salt and the calcium and magnesium compounds dissolve, leaving behind the clay and sand in the form of a muddy deposit which settles to the bottom of the tank. The hot solution is then pumped or poured into shallow iron pans and allowed to cool when the nitrate separates out with about only 1 per cent common salt, leaving the other substances in solution. The crystals of nitrate which sink to the bottom are strained off, then scooped out and allowed to dry in the air. They are then packed in 200 pound bags and are ready for the market. Analysis shows them to be about 95 per cent pure.

It is not possible to go into the technical details in a volume of this type of the extraction operation, which is not as simple as would appear from the above brief description. Many problems are encountered in attempting to make the operation as economical as possible. Such problems as fuel consumption, saving of water (an expensive item in the desert) by pumping the solutions from the crystallizing tanks back to the extraction tanks, utilization of the "fines", the prevention of muddy, turbid solutions by the clay of the caliche and many others, have led to the taking out of over 300 patents on extraction methods, on various forms of tanks, pumps, etc.

The above process, called the Shanks process, was introduced in 1876 and until some years after the World War, was almost exclusively used. At the present time it has been largely displaced by the Guggenheim process worked out along strictly scientific and engineering lines in the laboratories of Messrs. Guggenheim Brothers in New York.

THE GUGGENHEIM PROCESS

Whereas in the Shanks process there is much hand labor used, the Guggenheim process almost eliminates the workman and substitutes the machine. From the mining of the caliche to the bagging of the nitrate the machine does all the work, the workman is necessary only to direct it. The blasting of the costra is still done in much the same way as of old but from that time on the machine steps in. Large mechanical scrapers run by electricity from a central plant push off and pile up the costra, exposing the caliche. When this is blasted and loosened, electric shovels pick it up and deposit it, not one lump at a time as by the hand method, but half a ton or so at a time, into cars moving on temporary or semi-permanent tracks, to be conveyed to the crushers of the extraction plant.

On arrival at the plant, the loaded cars are mechanically tilted into huge crushers capable of handling some 1,200 tons of caliche an hour. The column of dust that rises from these crushers as the very dry caliche is being processed is visible ten miles away. It is one of the inevitable nuisances of a nitrate plant. The fine dust, carried by the wind, settles over the entire plant, covering everything with a layer half an inch thick particularly where there is any oil or water when thick crusts are formed. The caliche is crushed to pieces about the size of a large cherry. The "fines" which are inevitably produced, are sifted out and treated separately in a special section of the plant. From the crushers to the extraction tanks the caliche is carried by a continuously moving belt, a conveyor belt, which deposits its load in piles near the tanks. From these piles the electric loading bridges pick up the caliche and deposit it in extraction tanks.

The basic difference between the Shanks and the Guggenheim process of extraction is that the first uses *hot* water

Fig. 7—Laying temporary railway tracks.   Guggenheim process plant.

Fig. 8—Drilling preparatory to blasting of caliche bed.   Guggenheim process.

Fig. 9—Extraction tank. Guggenheim process.

Fig. 10—Mechanical unloading of spent caliche from extraction tank.
Guggenheim process.

and cools the solution of nitrates to atmospheric temperatures and the latter uses *warm* water and cools the solution
below atmospheric temperatures. The temperature range
in the Shanks process is between 72-280 degrees Fahrenheit,
while that in the Guggenheim process is between 50-104
degrees Fahrenheit. It requires, then, little fuel to heat
the solution and not much power to run a freezing plant to
do the cooling. As matter of fact, no direct fuel is used
as a source of heat but only waste heat from the huge Diesel
engines that furnish electric power to the plant. The water
which circulates around the cylinders of the Diesel motors
as it does in gasoline motors, to keep them cool, is warmed
sufficiently to heat the solution to the desired temperature.
A most efficient system to utilize all waste heat is one of
the outstanding features of this process. Solutions coming
to and from extraction tanks are passed through a system
of heat interchangers* where the solution that has been
cooled takes up heat again from one that is going to be cooled,
thus saving important amounts of fuel.

Another reason for using only warm solutions instead of
hot ones is that in that manner only the very soluble nitrate
is extracted and the lumps of caliche are not disintegrated.
The disintegration invariably leads to the formation of
muddy solutions from the clay content and from these it
is not possible without further operations to obtain a clean
looking nitrate.

The extraction tanks in the Guggenheim process are
huge concrete tanks, each holding 7,500 tons of caliche.
The solutions that leave them are pumped to crystallizing
tanks and gradually cooled through heat interchangers.
The temperature range has been chosen after long experimentation so that only the nitrate will crystallize out,
leaving other salts like common salt and magnesium salts
in solution. The nitrate is then separated out in centrifugal
machines that free it from the adhering solution and washed

---

*A heat interchanger is essentially a vessel partitioned off into two compartments
by a metal wall. The warmer liquid is made to circulate on one side of the wall and
the cooler one on the other. The liquids never mix but heat passes through the metal
wall from the warmer to the cooler one.

with a little water. After drying, it is pure white and analyzes to 98.5 per cent pure nitrate. The solution from which the nitrate has crystallized, the mother liquor as it is technically known, is then warmed up again through heat interchangers and pumped back to a new extraction tank. The solution is then really acting as if it were a belt conveyor. It picks up nitrate from the caliche, deposits it in the crystallizers and goes back again to begin its cycle.

The nitrate from the crystallizers though quite pure for all purposes is unfortunately in the form of very small crystals, like table salt. In such a state it absorbs moisture from the air readily; hence it is unfit for shipping to moist climates as it tends to *cake* and form large solid lumps. To avoid this difficulty it is melted and sprayed into the air. It melts at a high temperature, 308° C., and when it comes in contact with the air it cools suddenly forming small round pellets, like small hail stones or buckshot. These are very easy to handle, pack well and are readily marketable, specially for farming purposes, for they can be spread on the fields either by hand or machinery. The spraying is done in large steel plate towers with sufficient air circulation to keep them cool. The nitrate pellets as they fall to the bottom of the tower are carried off by a conveyor belt to the bagging house where they are mechanically weighed and packed in 100 or 200 pound bags.

As in the description of the Shanks process, many technical details have been omitted, such as for example the handling of the "fines" or small particles of caliche obtained in the initial crushing and the method of gradual extraction by placing tanks in series. All of these, extremely important from the point of view of plant economy, are beyond the aims of this book.

The Guggenheim process from the technical point of view is an outstanding achievement of modern chemical engineering. Unfortunately, it carries with it the curse of the highly mechanized process, the overhead. Two large plants have been built, the Maria Elena plant with an annual capacity of 600,000 tons of nitrate and the Pedro de Valdivia plant with a capacity of 700,000 tons. These two plants are said to have cost close to $70,000,000 and never to have operated to full capacity, thus laying a heavy burden of capital charges on the nitrate produced. The Maria Elena plant, which has been in operation since 1926, has never shown a profit, but rather a deficit estimated at $2,000,000 a year. Extensive modifications had to be made, owing to unforeseen difficulties which further added to overhead charges. With the experience gained in this first plant, the second one, Pedro de Valdivia, was constructed and operations started in July, 1931, but no data are so far available as to its capacity to produce economically. It is to be noted, however, that this enormous investment was made with utter disregard of the rapid and continuous increase in efficiency of synthetic nitrogen production.

At the present time, with low consumption and low prices of nitrogen, these overhead charges are crushing, making the manufacturing costs too high to permit competition with synthetic nitrogen.

PRESENT STATUS OF THE INDUSTRY

The Chilean nitrate industry has fallen on evil days in the last few years. Following the highly prosperous war years it has found its European markets gradually closing. It was mentioned above that the raid of von Spee's squadron off the Chilean coast had taught the nations of the world a memorable lesson. European nations have since the war made colossal efforts to prevent their ever being caught again in such a predicament. One by one they have built up their synthetic nitrogen plants so that they could at any time call upon them for their entire nitrogen supply. The United States has taken similar precautions. Naturally, to prevent the Chilean monopoly with its vast resources from ruining their infant industry, not only have tariff barriers been set up all over Europe but embargoes on the importation of Chilean nitrate as well.

At the present time Egypt and the United States are the only nations where Chile has a free market of importance unhampered by any duty or embargo.

From a controlling position twenty-five years ago when it supplied the world with 75 per cent of its total nitrogen consumption, the Chilean industry supplies, according to the latest statistics (1930-31), only 15 per cent. From all available information, in the fiscal year 1931-32 which closed on June 30th, the percentage will be far smaller as less than one million tons have been sold. If some cataclysm had wiped out the Chilean nitrate industry twenty-five years ago, the effects would have been catastrophic for the chemical and fertilizer industries of the world. If such a cataclysm should occur today, not a ripple would be felt in those industries, for synthetic and by-product nitrogen can take care of almost double the present world consumption.

To save the rapidly vanishing industry attempts were made in 1929 to organize a world nitrate cartel with Germany and Great Britain. An accord was signed in Berlin between the Chilean Government and the Interessen Gemeinschaft Farbenindustrie (the German Chemical Trust), later ratified in Paris by the Imperial Chemical Industries, Ltd. (the British Chemical Trust). Though German and British interests were fully capable industrially and financially to compete with Chilean nitrate, they did not relish the idea of lowering prices which the Chileans threatened to do. But, as in all cartels, the "outsiders", France, Belgium, Italy and the United States, and others, which controlled about 32 per cent of the world synthetic production, spoiled the plan and proceeded to sell under the fixed prices. This led to another attempt to fix prices in 1930 which— after many conferences between the European producers and when these had come to an agreement, between them and the Chilean Government—led to the convention of August 7, 1930, signed in Paris between nine European countries and Chile. This new cartel, which provided for the maintenance of the 1930 prices and allotted production quotas among the signatories, lasted, however, less than a year and since that time there has been a scramble for markets with prices tumbling to the present levels. The

Nitrate Operations in
CHILE
before rationalization

Caliche Deposits
Manufacturing
Plants

By Joseph Johnson, Courtesy of "Fortune".

Fig. 11—The nitrate industry of Chile before the
organization of the Cosach.

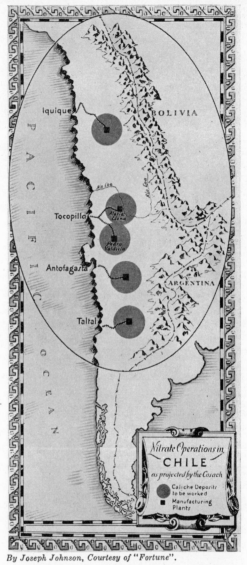

By Joseph Johnson, Courtesy of "Fortune".

Fig. 12—The nitrate industry of Chile as planned
by the Cosach.

United States producers declined to be represented at either of those conferences.

At the present time, Germany, France, Italy, Poland, Czechoslovakia, Belgium and Japan require special licenses to import Chilean nitrate, which means a practical embargo on that product.

The world industrial and agricultural depression has intensified the Chilean difficulties. Nitrate is not being exported to any great extent. Since 1928 stocks have been accumulating at the plants and at warehouses both in Chile and abroad. The exports to the United States have practically ceased. The main consumption of Chilean nitrate here was to be found among the cotton growers of the South, and these with 10,000,000 bales of unsold cotton on their hands are unable to finance purchases of much fertilizer.

The cheapness of other sources of nitrogen have made the sale of Chilean nitrate very difficult. With ammonium sulphate at $18 a ton, the cost of a ton of fertilizer nitrogen in that form is about $90, whereas with Chilean nitrate at $31 a ton, the cost of one ton of nitrogen is $186, or more than double. Clearly, though the objection to ammonium sulphate is that it "sours" the soil, an occasional application of lime would raise the cost of fertilizing with ammonium sulphate but a few dollars and make it a far cheaper fertilizer.

There are advantages for certain agricultural purposes in using sodium nitrate rather than ammonium salts but since sodium nitrate is now made synthetically by the American industry, Chilean nitrate finds increasing difficulties in maintaining its market here. This is strikingly shown by the figures of nitrate imports for March, 1932. In March, 1931, the United States imported 119,000 tons of nitrate from Chile, March being the month when sales to cotton planters are at or near the highest. In 1932, however, the imports fell to 47 tons, as the nitrate warehouses in New Orleans, Savannah, Jacksonville and Charleston were filled to capacity and unable to move their stocks. Imports for April and May

are of the same order of magnitude, 58 tons for April and
37 tons for May.

In 1930 the situation was so bad that a reorganization of
the nitrate industry became necessary. The industry consisted of a large number of "oficinas", or plants (Fig. 11)
more or less closely united by an association called the
Nitrate Producers Association, which was essentially a price-
fixing body. Under the pressure of increasing competition
from the synthetic industry it became evident that Chilean
nitrate production could not continue unless centralization
was effected.

The nitrate industry was in the hands of forty-five companies, all of them, except the Anglo-Chilean Consolidated
Nitrate Corporation—a concern controlled by the Guggenheim interests—using the old Shanks process. With the
backing of the Chilean Government a $360,000,000 trust
was formed in 1931, absorbing forty of these companies.
The trust was known as Compañia de Salitre de Chile, or,
as it is usually abbreviated, the Cosach. The Government
entered into partnership with the trust and agreed to elimi-
nate the export tax after 1933 in return for $180,000,000
of the $300,000,000 common stock of the company. It
furthermore agreed to take bonds of the company for a
total amount of 366,000,000 Chilean pesos ($46,000,000 at
the rate of exchange prevailing at the time) in lieu of the
export tax for the years 1931, '32 and '33. By special law
passed by the Chilean Congress, these bonds could be sold
by the Government to the Central Bank of Chile, which was
authorized to carry them as part of its gold reserve. The
balance of the common stock and $60,000,000 of preferred
were distributed in payment for the property of the merged
companies. Bonds were also issued in payment for the
property of some of these companies. The Cosach, in addition, assumed the obligations of these absorbed companies,
mostly 6 and 7 per cent bonds sold to investors here and
abroad, as follows:

Anglo-Chilean Consolidated Ni-
trate Corp. $54,000,000
Lautaro Nitrate, Ltd. . . . 43,000,000
Other companies 13,000,000
_____
$110,000,000

The company's plans, which were immediately put into
effect, contemplated closing the majority of the smaller
oficinas and concentrating production in five areas. (See
map in Fig. 12.) But even that plan proved too optimistic,
for, except at the Tocopilla and Antofagasta areas, production has now practically stopped.

When the Cosach was organized it was figured that the
cost of nitrate at the plant would be about $6 a ton, which,
with the addition of ten dollars for bagging, freight to port
and ocean freight, would make the cost, delivered at consumer's port, $16 a ton. Assuming an annual production
of 2,600,000 tons of nitrate, the overhead charges ($25,200,-
000) added $9.69 to the ton cost, making it $25.69. By
selling the nitrate at $37.25, the company could show a
profit of 10 per cent on the common stock. How far those
assumptions have proved incorrect is shown by the fact
that the nitrate production has fallen to about 1,700,000
tons in 1930-31. The storage and interest charges on stored
nitrate have further increased the losses of the company.

The indebtedness of the company on May 29, 1932 was
placed by the Chilean Minister of the Interior at what he
termed the "astronomical figure" of $158,302,562 and
£21,656,342—part of the debt being contracted in U. S.
dollars and part in British pounds. The interest and sinking
fund charges on this debt amount to $32,000,000 a year and
with the sales of nitrate at less than 1,000,000 tons for the
year 1931-32, the fixed charges would amount to over $32
per ton. Even if the original estimate of $16 per ton delivered
at consumer's port without fixed charges is taken as approximately correct, the nitrate would have to sell for $48 a ton
to cover costs and at no profit. The 1932 price has been

near the level of $31 a ton, until August when the price was dropped in the American market to $21.00 a ton. The company is therefore heavily "in the red", has defaulted on its bonds as well as on the bonds of its subsidiaries, the Lautaro and Anglo-Chilean.

THE CHILEAN GOVERNMENT AND THE NITRATE SITUATION

The hardship that the execution of the plan of the Cosach brought to the nitrate-bearing section of Chile is appalling. Tens of thousands of workmen and their families have been reduced to the verge of starvation, for the barren desert lands can supply neither food nor drinking water. The Chilean Government bravely faced the situation and has done its best to transport the starving population to the fertile plains in the south and settle them there in small farms, but the problem is a serious one. These people are entirely unacquainted with vegetation, which most of them may have only seen in the small parks of the larger cities or the gardens of the wealthier company officials who could afford the luxury of watering their lawns with distilled water. They are about as competent to do farm work as our average city dweller would be to take charge of an ostrich farm when his only acquaintance with the bird may be derived from having occasionally caught a glimpse of it at the Zoo. Their plight is indeed a sad one and the task of starting them in a new life presents serious and harassing problems.

The Chilean nitrate situation is further aggravated by its close connections to the Chilean Government finances. About 30 per cent of the Government's income was derived from the nitrate tax. If this tax could not be collected, the Government could not meet its debt obligations. It has now defaulted on its bonds and been forced off the gold standard.

Banking interests alien to the nitrate industry have become necessarily concerned in its maintenance at any cost for the sake of the loans they have floated. The copper interests in Chile, fearing their taxes would be increased to make up the nitrate tax deficiency, are closely watching developments, and since much American and foreign capital is invested in Chile in various enterprises, which would be rescued with difficulty if one of the principal assets of the country be eliminated, the problem has become one of serious diplomatic concern. It has now assumed international proportions, with Great Britain and the United States having preponderant interest in the matter.

Furthermore, the plants, which should have closed down for at least one year if run as independent commercial enterprises, are unable to do so as the Government compels them to keep going to prevent further increase in the unemployment situation. The nitrate cannot be moved even from the plants which have to continue accumulating stocks and increasing their losses.

A general reorganization of the company is now contemplated to reduce as far as possible the overhead charges which have proved too heavy.

Owing to the unsettled conditions in Chile since the revolution in June, 1932, with changes in the Government almost every month, negotiations are difficult to conduct. The creditors and bondholders who have organized protective committees in England and the United States have no sooner come to an agreement among themselves and begun negotiations with the Minister concerned than a change of Government makes it necessary to begin all over again with a new Minister. The matter has now been dragging since February, 1932, and there is little likelihood that the proposed plan, which is discussed in Chapter V (see also Appendix VII), will be accepted by the present Government.

Political pressure from the owners of the smaller nitrate plants who were paid in stock, now worthless, is sure to be felt in the Chilean Congress thus rendering a solution still more difficult.

IODINE AS A BY-PRODUCT OF THE NITRATE INDUSTRY

It was mentioned above that besides the nitrate in the caliche the sodium iodate was also of value. Until recent years this has been the only economical source of iodine. Iodine is of great importance to the medical profession as an antiseptic both in its elementary form in alcohol solution (tincture of iodine) and in many of its compounds (iodoform, sodium iodide, etc.). The photographic industry uses small amounts as does also the chemical industry. But the consumption is not great, being only about 800-900 tons a year. This small amount is, however, very important. With an average production of 2,000,000 tons of nitrate a year Chile could produce annually 10,000 tons of iodine but it could not sell them as there is not sufficient demand. One single Guggenheim plant could supply the entire world requirement by recovering the iodine from the solutions after the nitrate crystallization. The iodine recovery sections of the plants are run only intermittently so as not to increase the stocks on hand beyond possibility of consumption, especially as before the centralization of the industry considerable stocks had accumulated. Were it possible to increase the consumption of iodine to the present plant capacity and maintain its present price ($4.25 a pound), the nitrate plants could be run for their iodine yield and the nitrate given away. But even this small monopoly is now threatened by the discovery of iodine in the salt water of oil wells and in some brines at various points in the United States, in quantities warranting commercial exploitation. Similar brines exist also in the Baku oil district in Russia and in Java.

It is too early to determine whether this new American industry, which is only a few years old, will be able to produce cheaply enough to compete with Chilean iodine, but at any rate, it is now a certainty that this country will not find itself entirely at the mercy of the iodine monopoly.

Chile's plight is indeed a sad one but its resources, even outside the nitrate industry, are vast and its people courageous and energetic. They will solve their own problems though the solution might involve the abandonment of the controlling position which they held so long in the nitrogen industry.

CHAPTER III

THE ATMOSPHERIC NITROGEN INDUSTRY

THE ARC PROCESS

The dire predictions of Sir William Crookes regarding the approaching exhaustion of the Chilean deposits, erroneous but stimulating, concentrated the attention of chemists on the problem of nitrogen fixation.

It had been shown since the end of the 18th century by the English chemist Cavendish that when an electric spark was passed through air for a long time, combination took place between the oxygen and the nitrogen which, as stated, was called at the time "dephlogisticated air". If the products of this combination were absorbed in a solution of potash, saltpetre or nitre was obtained. Because of this experiment the chemist Chaptal later changed the name of "dephlogisticated air" to nitrogen from the Greek words *nitro* (nitre) and *gennao* (I give rise to). These experiments served as a basis for some earlier attempts to fix atmospheric nitrogen.

That nitrates could be obtained by this method, there was no doubt. The only question involved was, could they be made profitably on an industrial scale?

The first process developed was patented by two American inventors, Bradley and Lovejoy, in 1901 and an experimental plant built at Niagara Falls which started operations in 1902. In the Bradley-Lovejoy process air was passed between a large number of electric arcs which were lighted and extinguished about fifty times a second. The oxides of nitrogen formed in the apparatus were then absorbed in water or caustic soda solution giving nitric acid or sodium nitrate according to which of the two were used. The amount of electrical energy consumed, however, was enormous, amounting to 14,000 horsepower hours for every ton of nitric acid produced. After two years of experimentation the process was abandoned as too costly.

Almost simultaneously with the Bradley-Lovejoy process, two Norwegians, Birkeland and Eyde, patented a process for fixing nitrogen by the arc method. Birkeland, who was professor of physics at the University of Christiania (Oslo), had found that if the flame of an electric arc was submitted to the action of a powerful electromagnet, it would spread out to the shape of a flat disk. He conceived the idea that with this type of arc the formation of nitric oxide from air would be more efficient, and with the help of Eyde, a distinguished engineer, designed special apparatus for its utilization in fixing nitrogen.

While this development was going on, two Germans, Schönherr and Hesseberger, patented a third process, differing from the Birkeland-Eyde mainly in using an elongated arc flame instead of a circular one. In both these processes the nitric oxides formed in the arc were absorbed in water or alkaline solutions as in the Bradley-Lovejoy process.

Only a small amount of the air passed through the arc was changed to oxides of nitrogen, less than 2 per cent, but this was not an important drawback, since the raw material cost nothing. The consumption of electric power, however, was very great, and made it impossible to use either of these processes except in specially favored localities where large amounts of water power were available to produce electric power very cheaply. Such localities were found at Notodden and Rjukan in Norway, where these processes were installed and worked successfully for nearly twenty years, marketing their product as calcium nitrate, an excellent fertilizer made by treating nitric acid with limestone. These plants have now been converted to the more economical Haber process of nitrogen fixation.

Smaller installations using these arc processes, and a later one called the Pauling process, using a different shape of arc, were set up in Germany, Austria, France, Italy and the United States but were never worked more than a few years.

Fig. 13—Red hot cyanamide ingots in the cooling shed of a cyanamide plant.

Courtesy of *The Fertilizer Review.*

Fig. 14—Liquid air building of a cyanamide plant.

The arc method of nitrogen fixation has now become of insignificant importance and is of interest only from the historical point of view.

THE CYANAMIDE PROCESS

The process of fixing nitrogen by the formation of calcium cyanamide was discovered by two German chemists, Frank and Caro, in 1895. As stated in Chapter I, the process consists in passing nitrogen over calcium carbide at an elevated temperature. Calcium carbide is a compound made by heating coke and lime in an electric furnace, and was widely used in former years for making acetylene gas, which is given off from the carbide when water acts upon it.

In working this process under an industrial scale, the carbide is first ground to a fine powder, charged into large cylindrical ovens, heated to 1,600-1,800 degrees Fahrenheit, and then nitrogen passed into the oven at a slightly higher pressure than the atmospheric, for 18-24 hours. The carbide absorbs 18-20 per cent of its weight of nitrogen, forming calcium cyanamide and liberating half of the original carbon with which the calcium was combined. The addition of small percentages of calcium chloride or fluorspar (a mineral composed of the elements calcium and fluorine), hastens the absorption of the nitrogen by the carbide. The product comes out of the ovens in large cylindrical blocks which, after cooling, are crushed and powdered.

If the cyanamide is to be used as fertilizer, additional treatment is necessary, owing to the fact that some undecomposed carbide always remains, which, by the action of the moisture of the air, would generate acetylene gas. This would render the crude cyanamide dangerous to store, as explosions might easily occur. The difficulty is obviated by spraying the crude cyanamide with a little water, just enough to destroy the carbide, and mixing the product with a little crude oil to diminish the "dustiness". It is then bagged and marketed.

The cyanamide industry employs the nitrogen of the air but, unlike the arc process, must first separate the oxygen as, at the high temperature of the ovens, the carbide would be destroyed by its action. In accomplishing this separation the same principle is employed as in the separation of alcohol from its water solution, namely, distillation. When two liquids having different boiling points are mixed and the mixture boiled, the vapors given off are at first richer in the lower boiling liquid and later in the higher boiling one. By gradually cooling these vapors in special forms of condensers called "fractionating columns", it is possible to separate them each practically free from the other. This separation can be accomplished, however, only with liquids; since air is a gas, it must be first liquefied by pressure and strong cooling. Liquid oxygen boils at –182.5 degrees centigrade (296.5 degrees below zero Fahrenheit) and nitrogen at –195.5 degrees centigrade (319.9 degrees below zero Fahrenheit), at ordinary atmospheric pressure. With the very efficient fractionating columns that have been devised it is possible to separate the two quite completely. The liquid nitrogen is then allowed to evaporate, use being made of the intense cold which is developed in passing from the liquid to the gaseous condition, to liquefy more air. It is then stored in a gasometer ready for use in the cyanamide ovens. Seventy-four per cent of the weight of liquid air is due to nitrogen, and a large tonnage must be liquefied for, let us say, a plant fixing 80,000 tons of nitrogen a year. For such a plant over 300 tons of air must be liquefied every day, when the plant is running to capacity.

Calcium cyanamide is an excellent fertilizer, but for some reason has not achieved in the United States the success it has had in Europe. The European farmers have learned to use it, and, despite the predictions made some seven years ago that the cyanamide industry was gradually dying out, cyanamide has so far held its own in competition with other fertilizers.

The disadvantages of its use are first, that it is unpleasant to handle. The destruction of the excess of carbide when the fertilizer is being prepared forms free lime, which attacks the skin of the hands. The presence of the finely divided carbon which forms when the nitrogen reacts on the carbide is also an objection as it penetrates the pores of the skin and is difficult to remove.   Furthermore, in dry seasons, when not enough moisture is present in the soil to decompose the cyanamide, complex products are formed which are more or less toxic to the plants.

There is no calcium cyanamide manufactured in the United States at the present time.   The Muscle Shoals plant, a cyanamide plant built during the War with a capacity of 40,000 tons of nitrogen a year, has not been in operation since early in 1919.   In Canada, the American Cyanamid Company operates a plant at Niagara Falls with a capacity of 80,000 tons of nitrogen a year.   The capacities of other countries are as follows:

Capacities of Cyanamide Plants in Net Tons of Nitrogen

Czechoslovakia...	6,000	Norway.........	15,000
France..........	36,000	Poland..........	30,000
Germany........	114,000	Roumania.......	5,000
Italy...........	22,000	Sweden.........	6,000
Japan..........	63,000	Switzerland.....	5,000
Jugoslavia.......	14,000		

Though the total annual world capacity of cyanamide plants is 436,000 tons of nitrogen, the total production in 1931 amounted to only 200,000 tons which, however, is as good a showing as other nitrogen fixation processes have made during the depression.

During the war calcium cyanamide was extensively used as a source of ammonia.   By heating the cyanamide with steam under pressure ammonia is evolved and this, as will be shown later, can be made to combine with oxygen and water to form nitric acid.   At the present time, however, the manufacture of ammonia by this process has been largely superseded by the cheaper Haber process.

THE HABER PROCESS

A contemporary of Sir William Crookes, Professor Georg Lunge of the Zurich Polytechnicum, a distinguished authority in coal tar and by-product ammonia, and like Sir William given to long range predictions, prophesied in the early years of this century that the only source of ammonia that humanity could look forward to was by-product ammonia from coal, for he wrote:

"The synthetical production of ammonia from atmospheric nitrogen must find its limits in the impossibility of producing the requisite enormous amount of electrical energy *ad infinitum*, whether by water-power or otherwise. As far as we can look forward, the principal source of ammonia will be always the nitrogen of coal, just as this has been the case for a long time past."

Little did he realize that even as he was issuing his prophecy the foundations were being laid in many chemical laboratories for the development of that astounding process, the Haber process, which at the present time could turn out more ammonia in one year than all the by-product coke ovens in four.

That hydrogen and nitrogen could be made to combine to form ammonia by passing an electric spark for long periods through a mixture of three volumes of hydrogen and one of nitrogen had been known since the last quarter of the 18th century. It was also shown later that if ammonia gas were passed through a red hot tube, it would decompose giving three volumes of hydrogen and one of nitrogen. But a close study of this decomposition showed that there always remained a small amount, "a trace" as the chemist would say, of the original ammonia which could never be made to decompose. That little trace caused much scientific controversy. Why would it not be decomposed like the rest? Give it enough time and it will, said some. But it was also shown that if a mixture of three volumes of hydrogen and one of nitrogen were passed through a red hot tube, a trace of ammonia would form, especially if the tube were an iron tube. Not until the end of the 19th and the beginning of the 20th century could the matter be explained, for chemical theory had not sufficiently developed to handle the problem. The presence of that trace of ammonia gas, whether one

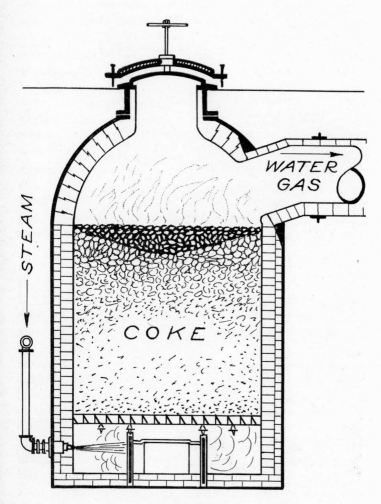

Fig. 15—Water gas generator

Fig. 16—A 21-unit water gas generator building in a synthetic ammonia plant.

Fig. 17—Top view of the 21 water gas units in the above building. The smaller units have capacities around 2,000,000 cubic feet, the larger ones up to 10,000,000 cubic feet of gas per 24 hours.

started with ammonia and decomposed it or started with hydrogen and nitrogen and caused them to combine, to the extent of a trace and never more, showed to the chemist that at the temperature of the red hot tube (about 800 degrees Centigrade) the reaction had "come to equilibrium" which meant that the three constituents, ammonia, hydrogen and nitrogen, must exist in those proportions and those proportions only at the atmospheric pressure under which those experiments were conducted. If one started with the hydrogen and nitrogen mixture they would combine to a slight extent and if one started with ammonia gas it would decompose almost entirely but in the end exactly the same proportions of the three, ammonia, nitrogen and hydrogen would be found.

Professor Fritz Haber of the Technische Hochschule of Carlsruhe, and his pupils undertook the accurate study of this equilibrium about 1905 and his work was followed by later investigations of Professor Walter Nernst of the University of Berlin, and his co-workers. Not only were the temperatures varied but the pressures also. These investigators found that when the nitrogen-hydrogen mixture was heated under pressure up to 70 atmospheres greater and greater amounts of ammonia would form. For example, at 400 degrees Centigrade and 10 atmospheres pressure the percentage of ammonia at equilibrium is 3.85 but at 50 atmospheres it is 15.27. The equilibrium, however, is very slowly reached by the gases alone, but if there is present a "catalyst", a substance which for some reason not well understood hastens the arrival of the equilibrium without taking any part in the reaction itself, the formation of ammonia was fairly rapid.

We do not know much about "catalysts" nor why they act; all we know is that they do and when setting out to find one suitable to hasten a particular reaction, practically the only method is the "hit-and-miss" method. A large number of substances must be tried until, sometimes most unexpectedly, one is found that accomplishes the desired result. The calcium chloride and the fluorspar added to the carbide in the manufacture of cyanamide are examples of catalysts. In the case of the reaction between nitrogen and hydrogen, iron furnishes the desired catalyst. Catalysts are of very great importance in chemistry and we shall meet them at almost every turn in surveying the atmospheric nitrogen industry.

In 1908 Haber's laboratory experiments began to interest the Badische Anilin und Soda Fabrik, Germany's richest and most powerful chemical company. The more they looked into the matter, the more they became interested, for there was apparently a process for "fixing" nitrogen which gave directly a very valuable product. They finally threw all their financial resources and their highly trained staff of chemical and engineering experts into the work of applying these experiments to the commercial production of ammonia and achieved in five years one of the greatest triumphs of chemical industry.

By 1913 a plant had been erected at Oppau, near the site of the great Badische works at Mannheim on the Rhine, with an annual capacity of 10,000 tons of ammonia, and this capacity was rapidly expanded.

It has been suggested that not until the Haber process had reached a commercial scale of operation did Germany dare to go to war. For with the practical certainty of being cut off from the Chilean nitrate deposits by the British fleet, it would have been suicidal on her part to risk finding herself unable either to manufacture munitions or fertilize her fields.

All other processes so far brought out for the synthesis of ammonia, the Claude process, the Casale process and many others, are only modifications of the Haber process, differing in using higher or lower pressures, condensing the ammonia by liquefaction instead of solution in water, difference in the catalyst used, etc. Basically, they are all the same. They consist in passing a gas mixture of three volumes of hydrogen and one of nitrogen under pressure and a fairly high temperature over a catalyst usually a porous iron mass specially prepared.

As a source of nitrogen, some Haber process plants employ, as the cyanamide process, liquid air. Since 82 per cent of the weight of ammonia formed is due to the weight of nitrogen, the liquid air plant is a most important adjunct of these Haber plants. In others, the nitrogen is obtained by passing air through a bed of red-hot coke when the oxygen is burned out to carbon dioxide, and the mixture of nitrogen and carbon dioxide is separated by dissolving out the soluble carbon dioxide in water. Carbon dioxide is the well-known gas that bubbles out of soda water, and therefore is soluble in water, especially under pressure. The purified nitrogen is stored in a gasometer ready for use. It can be obtained quite pure (99 per cent) at a comparatively low cost by either of these processes.

In plants where hydrogen can be obtained cheaply the oxygen of the air is burned out with hydrogen forming water which can be readily separated leaving pure nitrogen as the residue. If more than the necessary amount of hydrogen is mixed with the air, there results after the burning of the oxygen a mixture of hydrogen and nitrogen which can be so adjusted as to give the 3:1 mixture necessary for the ammonia synthesis.

The possible use of flue gases, which consist essentially of a mixture of nitrogen and carbon dioxide, with impurities of carbon monoxide and sulphur compounds readily removable, is also being studied as a source of nitrogen.

The hydrogen is not so easy to obtain and harder to purify. About 70 per cent of the total cost of producing ammonia is absorbed by the cost of producing the necessary hydrogen. There are three important sources.

The first is the so-called "water gas", extensively used as illuminating gas in most of our cities. It is obtained by passing steam through a bed of red hot coke. Water being a compound of oxygen and hydrogen, reacts with the carbon of the red hot coke forming the deadly carbon monoxide gas and hydrogen. The "water gas" consists of a mixture of equal volumes of hydrogen and carbon monoxide, and it is to the presence of this carbon monoxide that the poisonous properties of illuminating gas are due.

The carbon monoxide is removed by changing it to carbon dioxide. This is done by passing it with steam over a catalyst, usually oxide of iron, when carbon dioxide and more hydrogen are produced. As in the case of the preparation of nitrogen, the carbon dioxide can be dissolved out in water. This method of obtaining hydrogen is employed in most plants and accounts for 60 per cent of the total ammonia manufactured by the Haber process.

The second important source is the gas from the by-product coke ovens. This gas contains about 50 per cent hydrogen, the balance being gaseous compounds of hydrogen and carbon, the hydrocarbons. The hydrogen is separated by liquefying the hydrocarbons just as liquid air is liquefied, by pressure and cooling. The hydrogen, which cannot be liquefied except at extremely low temperatures, remains as a gas. The ammonia plants using this source of hydrogen must then be built in the neighborhood of large by-product coke ovens, and run in conjunction with them. This source produces about 23 per cent of the total Haber process ammonia.

The third important source is the decomposition of water by the electric current. This method gives a very pure hydrogen but is too expensive except in some very favorable localities where electric power is very cheap. About 15 per cent of the ammonia produced is made with this so-called "electrolytic hydrogen".

There are, in addition, several other methods of obtaining hydrogen. In many electro-chemical processes hydrogen is obtained as a by-product, and where sufficient quantities are available it is economical to use it for making ammonia. Only, however, about 1 per cent of the total synthetic ammonia is obtained from this source.

Many chemical processes for producing not only hydrogen but mixtures of hydrogen and nitrogen have been proposed, but so far none has been used on an industrial scale.

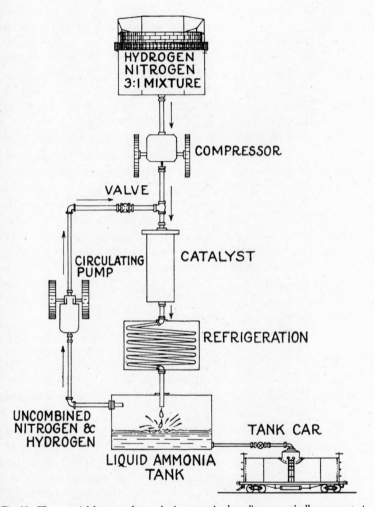

Fig. 18—The essential features of a synthetic ammonia plant diagrammatically represented.

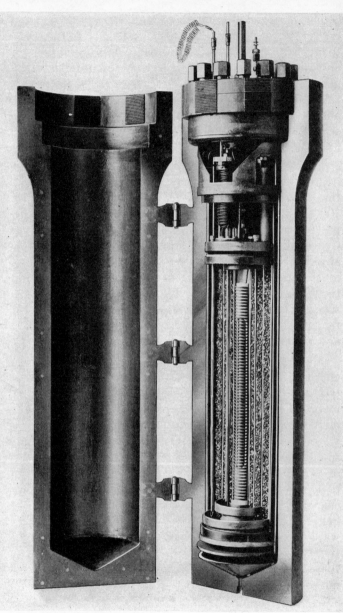

Courtesy of Fixed Nitrogen Research Laboratory.

Fig. 19—Model of a catalyst chamber showing internal arrangement of catalyst.

The hydrogen as obtained from all the above sources, except the electrolytic hydrogen, must be carefully purified to remove the last traces of carbon monoxide, carbon dioxide and any sulphur compounds that may be present. This is generally done by passing the hydrogen under pressure through vessels containing alkaline copper solutions which absorb the small amounts of these gases that the first separation methods could not completely remove. The pure hydrogen is then run to a gasometer for storage until needed.

The actual process of making ammonia once nitrogen and hydrogen have been obtained is comparatively simple, now that the reaction is understood. The gases are compressed to 100-400 atmospheres by specially designed compressors and passed over the catalyst initially heated to 300-400 degrees Centigrade (see Fig. 18). The reaction for the formation of ammonia evolves heat so that after the reaction begins not much heating is required. Since the pressure is comparatively high, the catalyzing chamber must be built of heavy special steel capable of resisting both the pressure and the temperature. A model of a catalyzing chamber cut open and hinged is shown in Fig. 19.

The catalyst is made by first fusing a natural pure oxide of iron, then breaking it to small fragments, heating it and treating it with hydrogen. As the oxide is changed to metallic iron by the hydrogen, it retains the original shape of the fragment, but, since the iron occupies a smaller volume than the original oxide, is pitted by innumerable small holes. The addition of small amounts (1 to 2 per cent) of other oxides, such as the oxides of aluminum and of potassium, has been found to make the catalyst more efficient. The catalyst, however, is very sensitive to "poisoning". Even small amounts of foreign substances, such as water vapor, carbon monoxide and sulphur compounds in the hydrogen-nitrogen mixture, destroy its efficiency; hence the necessity of carefully removing these from the gas mixture before passing it over the catalyst.

As the gas mixture issues from the catalyzing chamber, it contains varying percentages of ammonia depending on the temperature, pressure and the speed with which the gases are passed and these depend on the particular practice at any given plant. If the percentage of ammonia is small, less than 10 per cent, the ammonia is removed by absorption in water in which it is very soluble. If the percentage is higher, then the gases are cooled by refrigeration when the ammonia, which condenses to a liquid easily, is separated from the remaining gases. The hydrogen and nitrogen which have not combined are then sent back again over the catalyst by means of a circulating pump. The ammonia, whether in water solution or as liquefied anhydrous ammonia, then goes to storage tanks.

Ammonia is marketed chiefly in the form of its salts, the sulphate, the nitrate and the phosphate, but large amounts are also sold either as liquid anhydrous ammonia or as the water solution—so-called "ammonia water".

The solubility of ammonia in water is very great. One cubic foot of water will dissolve about 850 cubic feet of ammonia gas at a temperature of 50 degrees Fahrenheit and over 1,100 cubic feet at freezing temperatures. These figures apply only to atmospheric pressures for if the pressure of the ammonia over the solution is increased, the solubility will increase also. On warming the ammonia water, the ammonia gas is given off so that at boiling temperatures very little will remain dissolved.

The ammonia water is marketed in tank cars of ordinary type. Lately, however, the liquefied anhydrous ammonia has become of increasing importance. It requires only a pressure of 12-15 atmospheres to maintain ammonia in the liquid condition at ordinary temperatures and special railroad tank cars have been built to resist those pressures (see Fig. 25, page 62). At the present time it can be bought in the United States in 50,000 pound tank cars for as little as four and a half cents a pound.

So cheaply is liquid anhydrous ammonia obtained nowadays that it is being used *as a source of hydrogen*. This seems paradoxical but it is nevertheless a fact. Many metallurgical processes need to use hydrogen but not in sufficiently large amounts to warrant the erection of a plant large enough to produce it economically. Formerly the hydrogen was transported to these consumers in heavy steel cylinders under 100 atmospheres pressure. The transportation costs per cubic foot of hydrogen were high, as not only had the cylinders to be transported to the plant but sent back again to the producer. By passing ammonia through a hot tube, however, a mixture of practically three volumes of hydrogen and one of nitrogen is produced and as the nitrogen is a very inert gas, it does not interfere with most of these metallurgical operations.

At least three electrical manufacturing companies in the United States have now on the market "ammonia dissociators", consisting essentially of a tube heated electrically through which the ammonia gas is passed and decomposed into its elements. The liquid ammonia tanks and steel cylinders are of much lighter construction than the hydrogen ones and sufficient saving is effected in freight charges to make this method of producing hydrogen an economical one.

The development of the Haber process with certain variations of detail such as the higher pressures and temperatures employed by the Claude process (900 atmospheres and 800 degrees Centigrade) has been phenomenal. The initial 10,000 ton plant at Oppau was expanded during the war to a capacity of about 100,000 tons and another large plant, the Leuna plant, was started at Merseburg to supply the German war requirements of fixed nitrogen. The latter plant has grown to enormous proportions. It is the largest plant in the world and has now a capacity of 600,000 tons of fixed nitrogen per year. This amount is greater than the highest total export of nitrogen from Chile in any one year and 50 per cent higher than the average yearly tonnage exported.

The Haber process and its modifications have been installed in every important country in the world. Nowhere, however, is such a single large plant as the Leuna to be found, the nearest competitor in size being the plant at Hopewell, Va., which has a capacity of 177,000 tons of nitrogen per year. Table 2 gives the number of plants and yearly capacities in the producing countries of the world.

TABLE 2

Yearly Capacity of Synthetic Ammonia Plants in Net Tons of Nitrogen

Country	No. of Plants	Capacity
Belgium	6	132,000
Canada	1	17,500
Czechoslovakia	2	13,000
England	1	170,000
France	20	191,000
Germany	9	860,000
Italy	9	47,000
Japan	7	107,000
Jugoslavia	1	16,000
Netherlands	4	134,000
Norway	2	85,000
Poland	4	52,000
Russia	2	40,000
Spain	3	8,600
Sweden	1	2,000
Switzerland	1	7,500
United States	10	318,600

World capacity............ 2,201,200

Though the large plants can produce ammonia more economically than small ones it can be seen that there are few large plants in the world and many small ones. One of the chief necessities is a source of cheap hydrogen, which as already pointed out absorbs 70 per cent of the cost of manufacturing ammonia; hence smaller plants are justified in the neighborhood of coke ovens, sources of electrolytic hydrogen or very cheap electric power, provided, however, they be far enough from a large plant and have a market close at hand to take advantage of the differential in freight rates that would apply to the product of the large plant.

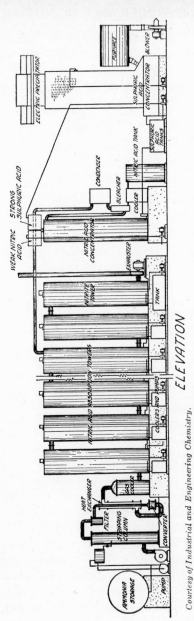

Courtesy of Industrial and Engineering Chemistry.

Fig. 20—Diagram of plant for oxidizing ammonia to nitric acid.

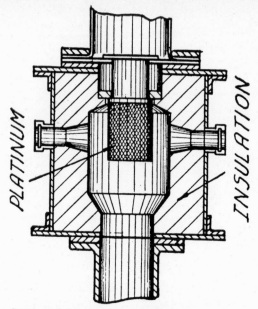

Courtesy of Industrial and Engineering Chemistry.

Fig. 21—Diagram of converter. Ammonia oxidation plant.

Courtesy of Fixed Nitrogen Research Laboratory.

Fig. 22—Converter building of ammonia oxidation plant.

FUTURE OF THE HABER PROCESS

The Haber process may be said to be in its early youth only. The great possibilities in its development lie in the cheapening of the sources of hydrogen which, as stated, accounts for 70 per cent of the cost of manufacturing ammonia by this process. The Leuna plant in Germany has already accomplished a considerable saving by using cheap lignite coal instead of coke in its "water gas" plant. On the Pacific coast a plant is now operating, using hydrogen obtained by the decomposition of natural gas, but details as to methods and costs are, unfortunately, lacking. It seems hardly possible, however, that the chemist will not be able to meet the challenge of such a high cost fraction and admit himself defeated in his attempts to lower the price of synthetic ammonia.

NITRIC ACID FROM AMMONIA

Ammonia is not of use only to the fertilizer industry. The chemical industry uses a large tonnage for manufacturing nitric acid, so important both to the industry itself, and to national defense.

The French chemist, Kuhlman, showed in 1839 that a mixture of air and ammonia gas could be changed to nitric acid by passing it over platinum and other substances, which acted as catalysts. At the time, however, these experiments were only of scientific interest, for there were no cheap sources of ammonia available, neither was there a sufficient demand for nitric acid to warrant their being commercially utilized. Some sixty years later the German chemist, Wilhelm Ostwald, developed a process for making industrial use of these experiments, which he patented in several countries outside of Germany but was unable to convince the German Patent Office of the originality of his invention. They pointed to Kuhlman's published work and refused to grant the patent. Ostwald found that the passing of the ammonia and air over a fine gauze woven of platinum wire "of silky fineness" brought about the desired result, and designed special apparatus and absorption towers to carry out his process.

Two plants were erected about 1910, one in Westphalia and another in Belgium, and though the process was kept more or less secret, they seem to have worked successfully, for dividends were paid up to 1913.

Soon after the outbreak of the War, Frank and Caro, the same chemists who had invented the calcium cyanamide process, developed a process for the oxidation of ammonia, using cyanamide as a source of ammonia instead of the gas works "ammonia liquor" which Ostwald had used. But even this process was promptly superseded by the huge nitric acid plants using synthetic ammonia which were rapidly erected in Germany, at Oppau, Merseburg, Hoechst and Leverkusen.

It is estimated that without these plants Germany could not have continued the war much after the spring of 1915, for her stocks of Chilean nitrate in August, 1914, amounted to only 500,000 tons, augmented in October by 100,000 tons captured at Antwerp. These would have been sufficient for little over six months, even taking into consideration the stocks of munitions she had on hand. It is estimated that her war requirements were 2,500,000 tons of nitrate a year, which had to come entirely from atmospheric nitrogen.

The process for making nitric acid from ammonia is now worked on a commercial scale both in this country and abroad. A typical plant is shown diagrammatically in Fig. 20. The process is worked as follows:

Air containing 10 per cent of ammonia by volume is passed into a "converter", the essential part of which is a platinum gauze cylinder through which the mixture must pass (Fig. 21). On coming in contact with the platinum the action begins, and as it liberates considerable amount of heat, the gauze becomes red hot. The reaction is an extremely rapid one. It is estimated that it takes only a little over one one-thousandth of a second for the mixture in contact with the platinum to change from ammonia and oxygen to nitric oxide and water.

A second reaction proceeds beyond the gauze and that is the formation of nitric dioxide from the action of the nitric oxide with more oxygen. The nitric dioxide is also a gas and when absorbed in water gives nitric acid as one of the products. This second reaction takes an appreciable time to proceed, and for that reason beyond the converter there is always provided a large chamber where the gases are cooled and time is allowed for the formation of nitric dioxide. From there the gases are passed into large absorption towers filled with pieces of quartz or earthenware material over which water continuously trickles. The nitric acid formed in these towers is only 45-60 per cent water solution, but more concentrated acid can be made by mixing this acid with sulphuric acid and distilling the mixture, when pure concentrated nitric acid is obtained.

There are several modifications of this process. Instead of a cylindrical gauze, a flat sheet of gauze, sometimes several sheets superimposed one on the other are used. Other processes use different catalysts, iron oxide, mixtures of iron and bismuth oxides, which are cheaper than platinum and said to be quite as effective. The initial investment in platinum for an ammonia oxidation plant is considerable, for as each converter can produce only a few tons of nitric acid per day, a large number must be provided for a large plant.

The gauze catalyst is so sensitive to "poisoning" by impurities that in some plants it becomes necessary to bring the air from a considerable distance to avoid its being contaminated by dust and flue gases invariably found in the neighborhood of factories.

It is not necessary to concentrate all the 45-60 per cent acid obtained from the absorption towers. It can be used as such for the preparation of ammonium nitrate, calcium nitrate and sodium nitrate by treating it with the necessary amount of ammonia, limestone, or with a cheap alkali such as "soda ash".

The synthetic sodium nitrate so obtained is identical with and in fact purer than the Chilean nitrate and is now produced in large quantities both in Europe and in the United States, cheaply enough to compete with the natural nitrate.

For the manufacture of explosives, concentrated nitric acid is necessary but since the munitions plants were equipped to manufacture nitric acid with Chilean sodium nitrate and sulphuric acid, it was the German practice in the war to provide the munitions plants with synthetic sodium nitrate and let them make their own nitric acid by the old process. This practice still holds to a great extent; hence the importance of the synthetic sodium nitrate from the standpoint of national defense.

OTHER PROCESSES FOR NITROGEN FIXATION

Nitrogen can be fixed by several other processes but as these are not utilized on a large scale comparable with those described only brief mention of them will be made.

The Bucher process fixes nitrogen by passing it over a mixture of sodium carbonate and carbon when sodium cyanide is formed. It is of interest that it was while studying this reaction that Frank and Caro discovered the cyanamide reaction. The cyanide is used as such in many industries, electroplating of metals and the extraction of gold from its ores, chiefly, and can also be changed to ammonia by treatment with steam. In view of the present cheapness of ammonia, however, this method is entirely out of the question. The cyanide cannot be used as a fertilizer, being a violent poison to plants as well as to animals.

There has been developed also another nitrogen fixation process which consists in forming aluminum nitride (a compound of aluminum and nitrogen) by heating bauxite, a naturally occurring oxide of aluminum, with coal and passing nitrogen over the mixture. The nitride on being decomposed with steam gives ammonia. This process, however, has not been as yet employed on an industrial scale.

CHAPTER IV

THE UNITED STATES AND THE NITROGEN PROBLEM

CONDITIONS BEFORE 1914

The American chemical industry labored before the European War against severe handicaps. The German chemical industry dominated the markets of the world. The United States, being one of her chief customers, her predominant position in this country would not be yielded without a struggle. Under the circumstances capital was timid to adventure into a field in which it would have to contend at the start with a powerful competitor, well equipped both from the financial and technical standpoints.

The coal tar industry, which the Germans had developed to such a fine point, was so closely held by them and hedged by so many patents taken out in this country—not with a view of working out their processes here but only to prevent any one else from using them—that the demand for coal tar in the United States was very small. The vast quantities of coke required by our steel industry were made almost entirely in the old, wasteful "beehive" coke ovens. It is not so long ago that travelers coming into or leaving at night such a steel center as Pittsburgh would see the sky lighted up for miles by the flames of the "beehive" coke ovens wasting millions and millions of dollars of valuable tar, gas and ammonia. But few dared to affront the risk of competing with the German chemical combinations and install the by-product coke ovens that had completely supplanted the old "beehive" ones in Europe for nearly thirty years.

Little by-product ammonia was obtained in the United States before 1914. The capacity was but 40,000 tons of nitrogen against a present one of 200,000 tons. There was no synthetic nitrogen production. The Bradley-Lovejoy process had lasted but two years and though the American Cyanamid Company had installed the largest cyanamide plant in the world at Niagara Falls, it had been built on the Canadian side and could not properly be counted as a part of our national industry. We were entirely dependent on Chile for our nitrates and on Europe for most of the necessary by-product ammonia.

THE OUTBREAK OF THE EUROPEAN WAR

When war broke out in 1914 and we found ourselves isolated from our former source of supplies of dyes, pharmaceuticals and numerous other coal tar derivatives, the industries dependent on those products were faced with a shortage that we had no means to relieve. When the prospects of a short war faded out after the first few months and orders for munitions for the Allied armies began to pour into the United States, the necessary materials were not to be had in amounts sufficient to supply the demands. Toluol and carbolic acid, obtained from coal tar and needed for high explosives, reached fantastic prices, as did the coloring matters for which the textile industry clamored loudly. Our physicians and hospitals could not find at any price the drugs which they needed and which had been produced by patented processes in Germany. At last the country understood the warnings which Government agencies, like the Bureau of Mines, and the chemical profession in general, had been issuing for years against our wasteful methods of coking coal. The death knell of the "beehive" was sounded, but it took a major catastrophe to make us understand.

The construction of by-product coke ovens, however, is not an industrial development that can be carried out overnight, and though such construction was promptly started, production of by-product ammonium sulphate had only doubled by the end of the War.

We had at the time no plants to oxidize ammonia and Chile saltpetre was our only source of nitric acid. This absolute dependence on the Chilean monopoly was brought out in the annual report of the Chief of Ordnance of the United States Army in 1915. The necessity of our developing other sources was only too apparent. At any time we might be cut off by German submarines and the sinking of even a few ships loaded with nitrates would seriously interfere with our industries and agriculture. The possibilities of our entering the War were by that time being also seriously considered.

The report of the Chief of Ordnance made an impression on Congress, for in 1916 an appropriation of $20,000,000 was made for the development by the Government of nitrogen fixation. A committee of scientists and engineers was appointed to study and report on the matter.

In the meantime, the General Chemical Company, later merged into the Allied Chemical & Dye Corporation, had started an experimental synthetic ammonia plant at Laurel Hill, Long Island, using a process similar to Haber's, but a different catalyst. The plant gave us the first glimpse of the promised land of nitrogen independence, and in it was trained the organization which first produced synthetic ammonia on a commercial scale in this country and was later to build the second largest plant in the world. We had made a beginning.

THE CHILEAN NITRATE SITUATION, 1917-1918

Not only were we entirely dependent on Chile for nitrates at the beginning of the War, but we remained so for the entire duration of hostilities, for the total amount of synthetic nitrogen produced was negligible compared to the actual requirements. The producers and speculators in Chile could have exacted almost any price for their nitrate but for a fortuitous circumstance which they were not able to take into account.

A number of nitrate "oficinas" were owned and operated by German subjects who could not sell to the Allies nor to us, after we declared war, because of the Trading with the

Enemy Act, which forbade such transactions. In the Spring of 1917 speculators in Chile, figuring that the production and stocks of these German companies would be automatically tied up and unsalable, bought nitrates for delivery in October, November and December, running the price to $150 a ton and expecting to reap a rich harvest of profits when the demands for our Army became pressing in the fall. Our War Industries Board, which had control of the purchase of nitrates, would have had to meet that price but for a bit of secret information which reached them through our Naval Intelligence Bureau.

The Chileans, who had for many years been great admirers of the Germans, had their country's gold reserve on deposit in Berlin and when they sought to withdraw it, in the spring of 1917, the German Government informed them that they would not be permitted to do so. As soon as this became known, through the above-mentioned Bureau, the United States Government entered into negotiations with the Chileans, offering to restore their gold reserve, provided the Chilean Government would seize the German-owned nitrate and sell it to the United States for $90 a ton. The offer was accepted, but the matter was kept secret for many difficulties had to be surmounted, such as the embargo on gold exports, the procuring of jute bags from India and the necessary tonnage to deliver the nitrate. These, however, were finally overcome and when shipments began in October the speculative market collapsed and nitrate was offered at $90 a ton in sufficient amounts to supply not only our own needs but those of our Allies also.

Later the entire nitrate purchasing power for all the Allied armies was centralized in one single office, thus avoiding competitive bidding. For the balance of the War nitrates were bought at an average of $82.50 a ton. Considering that production costs were but about $27 a ton plus a Government tax of $12 a ton, a handsome profit was realized by the Chileans.

The important points to be remembered are how completely dependent we were on this monopoly and that this

Courtesy of Ordnance Department, U. S. Army.

Fig. 23—The Wilson dam at Muscle Shoals.

Courtesy of Ordnance Department, U. S. Army.

Fig. 24—Nitrate plant No. 1 at Sheffield, Alabama.

dependence was only partly shaken by our opportune knowledge of the gold reserve episode.

In the years 1917 and 1918 we imported 1,728,398 tons and 2,066,483 tons, respectively, making a total of nearly 3,800,000 tons. For this we paid $323,000,000, of which nearly $40,000,000 went to pay the Chilean Government tax. But for the above-mentioned episode, this essential item of war material might well have cost us nearly double the amount.

THE BEGINNING OF OUR NITROGEN INDUSTRY

The committee of scientists and engineers appointed by Congress to look into the fixation of nitrogen filed its report in January, 1917. Before, however much could be done about its recommendations war had been declared and the problem of nitrogen fixation passed into the hands of the Ordnance Department of the Army which promptly organized a Nitrate Division to handle the matter.

As soon as we entered the War, German property in the United States was confiscated and the office of the Alien Property Custodian created to administer it. The office was organized and began to function in October, 1917. The enemy-owned patents, though not formally seized until November, 1918, became subject to being licensed to American manufacturers on application to the Federal Trade Commission, and many licenses were granted for a suitable fee which was paid to the Alien Property Custodian. There were about 5,000 patents taken out in this country by German chemical interests of which some 250 concerned nitrogen fixation. Most of the latter had not been taken out until 1916.

The Nitrate Division plans contemplated the building of two nitrogen fixation plants to which two more were added later to take care of increasing requirements. As the only process that was working in the United States even on an experimental scale, was the General Chemical Company process at Laurel Hill, negotiations were initiated with this company and Nitrate Plant No. 1 was ordered built to use this process at Sheffield, Alabama with an estimated capacity

of 9,000 tons of ammonia per year. As the army requirements were for nitrates and not for ammonia, an ammonia
oxidation plant was built close to the ammonia plant with
a capacity of 14,000 tons of nitric acid per year. The entire
project cost the Government $12,900,000. This included not
only the cost of the plant but the land, improvements and
the construction of a village to house the workmen and
the plant staff. The process utilized water gas as a source of
hydrogen. Only a small amount of ammonia, however, was
produced by this plant. The difficulties encountered were
not surmounted in time. Although the Haber patents went
into great detail as to apparatus, temperatures and pressures, the most essential part of the process, the catalyst
and the methods of preparing it were not given, hence long
researches were necessary to rediscover this essential feature.
The catalyst used by the General Chemical Company gave
poor results on large scale operation.

There was only one process for the fixation of nitrogen
on this continent that at the time had been worked successfully for years and that was the cyanamide process at Niagara
Falls, Ontario. Since information was already available as
to utilization of cyanamide to form ammonia and then to
use this ammonia to make nitric acid, the Ordnance Department decided that the safest course lay in availing ourselves
of this known process and accordingly plans were drawn
for a large cyanamide plant. This was to be Nitrate Plant
No. 2.

The manufacture of calcium carbide to make cyanamide
requires temperatures which can be reached only by the
electric furnace. Hence, considerable amounts of electric
power were necessary and as the power plants in existence
were all being utilized to capacity by the war industries, an
entirely new water power development was decided upon
and located on the Tennessee River at Muscle Shoals.
Construction of the cyanamide plant, the ammonia oxidation plant and the water power development began in
January, 1918 and operations started on October 26th of
the same year. The installation of this process cost the

Government $69,000,000 but only test runs were made as the Armistice had been signed before the plant could be run to capacity. The total production of this plant was only 2,200 tons of cyanamide and some 600 tons of nitric acid which includes test runs made after the Armistice. The plant has a rated annual capacity of 40,000 tons of fixed nitrogen (200,000 tons of cyanamide) and is capable of producing 78,000 tons of nitric acid a year. It has been maintained in a stand-by condition since 1919 but has never resumed operations.

Two more plants were started by the Ordnance Department for nitrogen fixation, Nitrate Plant No. 3 at Toledo, Ohio, and Nitrate Plant No. 4 at Broadwell, near Cincinnati. The construction work on these projects, however, was not begun until September, 1918 and the foundations had been hardly completed when the Armistice was signed. About $14,500,000 was spent on these projects part of which was salvaged when construction was stopped.

The existing Government plants for nitrogen fixation represent an investment of $81,000,000 and if in addition the cost of the water power development and electric substations is figured in, the investment would reach $127,000,000. On this to date there has been no financial return, but the experience gained and the training of competent staffs to run nitrogen fixation plants have been invaluable. As an offshoot of this powerful effort, there was organized a research department known as the Fixed Nitrogen Research Laboratory which has been in continuous existence to this day and has greatly contributed to the development of our nitrogen industry.

THE FIXED NITROGEN RESEARCH LABORATORY

So many problems came up during the construction and test runs of the nitrate plants that a research staff had to be organized to deal with them. Owing to insufficiency of funds, the research work had to be spread over several localities, at Sheffield near Nitrate Plant No. 1, at Arlington Farms, Virginia, and the laboratories of several commercial concerns and universities throughout the country. This work, however, was finally centralized in March, 1919, in the Fixed Nitrogen Research Laboratory which took up quarters in one of the buildings of the American University in Washington, D. C., where it is at present located. This organization was under the direction of the Ordnance Department until July, 1921, when it was transferred to the Department of Agriculture. The Laboratory is fully equipped to carry on research work under high pressures and to study the preparation and properties of catalysts. It has a staff of chemists and engineers who devote their time to the advancement of the scientific and practical knowledge of nitrogen fixation.

The influence of this institution in the development of our fixed nitrogen industry, which began shortly after the War to assume important proportions, can hardly be over-estimated. Not only were many research problems of vital concern to the industry solved in that laboratory, but there is hardly a synthetic nitrogen plant in the United States which does not have on its staff men who received their training in this very specialized field, at the hands of the distinguished chemists who have guided its destinies since the very beginning.

The Fixed Nitrogen Research Laboratory has not been the only source of progress in our nitrogen industry. The organization of another institution, The Chemical Foundation, has also been a powerful contributor.

THE CHEMICAL FOUNDATION

The strangle hold that the German chemical industry had on our chemical markets before the War was due not only to their ruthless methods of competition, propaganda and bribery, but to the unsurmountable obstacle of the ring of patents with which it was surrounded and with which it protected itself against any effort to start a chemical industry in the United States.

As stated above, the German patents had been seized by the Alien Property Custodian as enemy property in 1918.

In order to protect the chemical enterprises, worth millions of dollars, that had been started here in an endeavor to supply our war requirements, and which surely would have been stifled after peace was declared, the idea was conceived to place all these seized patents in trust for the use of the American chemical industry.   Accordingly, a corporation was organized by a group of outstanding personalities to buy these patents from the Alien Property Custodian and administer them for the benefit of the American chemical industry, granting licenses on equal terms to all American manufacturers for a small royalty and free of charge to the Government.   The corporation was organized in Delaware in February, 1919, and capitalized at $500,000, of which $400,000 was 6 per cent cumulative preferred stock and $100,000 common stock limited to 6 per cent dividends. Profits derived from patent royalties were to be devoted to the retirement of the preferred and any excess over the requisite amount to be used for the advancement of chemical and allied arts and industries in the United States.   Thus The Chemical Foundation, Inc., came into being.

The organization of this corporation was the first forward step towards that freedom from foreign domination which has at last been achieved by our chemical industry.   Without going into details of the general beneficial effect directly derived from the organization of The Chemical Foundation, it must be pointed out that without it this country would at present be dependent on importations of nitrogen for at least one-half of its requirements, for Haber patents taken out in the United States in 1916 would prevent any one from using this process until 1933.   Because of the vesting of the patent rights in The Chemical Foundation, their use has resulted in our developing a source of synthetic nitrogen capable of taking care of almost all our requirements.   The royalty charged by the Foundation for the use of its 250 patents dealing with nitrogen fixation is but one dollar per ton of the ammonia manufactured and their use is open to all responsible individuals or corporations.   These royalties will cease in October, 1933, when the patents will expire.

No payments either as dividends or amortization have so far been made to stockholders of The Chemical Foundation and its principal officers have served without salary for the past thirteen years. The receipts from patent royalties have been devoted to the advancement of research in chemistry and allied subjects, pharmacology and medicine, either directly or through the financing of technical publications in those branches of science. The Foundation has done much also to arouse the interest of the layman in science by the publication of a number of books specially written in non-technical language.

COMMERCIAL DEVELOPMENT OF NITROGEN FIXATION

The close of the War found us very nearly where we were at the start in the production of atmospheric nitrogen. Not much had been achieved in actual production, but a vast amount of experience had been gained which during the following twelve years was to lead to a position of complete independence from foreign nitrogen. By 1921 only one plant, built by the Atmospheric Nitrogen Corporation at Syracuse, N. Y., was producing in appreciable amounts—3,000 tons of nitrogen annually,—by the Haber process. Within a few years, however, the number and capacity of the plants increased rapidly. Capacities in 1932 are as follows:

Corporation	Location	Net Tons Nitrogen
Atmospheric Nitrogen Corp.	Hopewell, Va.	177,000
E. I. du Pont de Nemours & Co.	Belle, W. Va.	100,000
Atmospheric Nitrogen Corp.	Syracuse, N. Y.	14,000
Shell Chemical Co.	Pittsburg, Cal.	10,000
Pennsylvania Salt Mfg. Co.	Wyandotte, Mich.	6,000
Mathieson Alkali Co.	Niagara Falls, N. Y.	5,000
Roessler-Hasslacher Chemical Co.	Niagara Falls, N. Y.	2,500
Midland Ammonia Co.	Midland, Mich.	2,000
Great Western Electrochemical Co.	Pittsburg, Cal.	1,200
Pacific Nitrogen Co.	Seattle, Wash.	900
	Total	318,600

Courtesy of The Fertilizer Review.

Fig. 25—Trainload of anhydrous ammonia leaving the Hopewell, Va., synthetic ammonia plant.

Fig. 26—Trainload of synthetic sodium nitrate leaving the Hopewell, Va., plant where it was manufactured

These plant capacities cannot be given with a claim to strict accuracy because of the rapid changes that are constantly going on, but they certainly represent a minimum capacity in 1932.

PRESENT NITROGEN SITUATION

With the substitution of by-product coke ovens for the old "beehive" ones our by-product ammonia annual capacity has now reached 200,000 tons of nitrogen. Adding this to the synthetic ammonia capacity in tons of nitrogen taken as 318,600, we have a capacity of 518,600 tons of nitrogen, which is far in excess of our normal peace-time consumption placed at 370,000 tons.

Military authorities place our nitrogen requirements for the manufacture of explosives and smokeless powders, in case of war, at 150,000 tons. This figure represents a maximum which will not be reached until the third year of a major war. That amount—and a good deal more—could be supplied by our existing plants which, without much difficulty, could step up their production at least 10 per cent above normal capacity.

From the military standpoint, since nitric acid is necessary for explosives, the ammonia oxidation units at Sheffield and Muscle Shoals might be necessary but, as these are kept in stand-by condition, they can be put to work at any time. Our commercial capacity for the production of synthetic sodium nitrate is now close to 900,000 tons a year, or nearly the total amount of nitrogen needed by the Army if this were all taken as nitrate. It is doubtful if even in an emergency the Muscle Shoals cyanamide plant or the Sheffield ammonia plant would be placed in operation, as the cost of modernizing them would be hardly justifiable in view of our plentiful and cheaper supplies of fixed nitrogen.

We have, then, reached the point where we can not only supply our own needs but have a surplus as well; in fact, during the latter part of 1931 and the first months of 1932, we have actually exported some 90,000 tons of American-made synthetic sodium nitrate. This is not a large amount, to be sure, but it is a significant development. From a negligible place as atmospheric nitrogen producers ten years ago, we can now boast the second largest plant in the world and a capacity that can take care of an expanding demand for several years to come.

The agricultural and industrial depression has been severely felt by the nitrogen industry. Prices of nitrogen have reached the lowest point on record. Whereas, before 1914, ammonium sulphate cost the fertilizer manufacturer $60 a ton, by 1931 the price had sunk to $38, and is now about $18-$20. (See Appendix VII.)

It is estimated, though no accurate information is available, that the total investment in synthetic nitrogen plants in this country is about $80,000,000. If we add to this amount the $81,000,000 spent by the Government on its nitrogen plants during the war, $161,000,000 have now been invested by the country in achieving nitrogen independence, an amount which is certainly worth while to surround with all possible safeguards.

GOVERNMENT OPERATED PLANTS

It has been proposed at various times that the Government should enter the manufacture of synthetic nitrogen by operating or causing to be operated its nitrogen fixation plants and sell the fixed nitrogen to the farmers at cost. This suggestion, which has been a political football for the past ten years, is one that requires very careful consideration.

Apart from the question as to whether a Government can operate any industry more cheaply than private ownership, it should be considered that, first of all, the Sheffield and Muscle Shoals plants are by this time out of date and could not produce fixed nitrogen as cheaply as existing modern plants. The capacities of both plants combined would be but some 47,000 tons of fixed nitrogen, or about one-seventh of our peace-time requirements. Both plants would have to be remodelled at an estimated cost of $15,000,000. With such a fund available, a Haber plant could be constructed to yield a larger tonnage of fixed nitrogen at a lower price than either the cyanamide Muscle Shoals plant or the Sheffield ammonia plant.

The ammonia oxidizing sections of these plants, however, constitute a real item of national defense and should be maintained, as they are now, in a stand-by condition, ready for an emergency.   Anhydrous liquid ammonia, which could be supplied by our industry in sufficient amounts for all military requirements, could be easily rushed to those plants which in a short time could begin producing nitric acid or ammonium nitrate for military requirements without any interference with the normal demands of our fertilizer or chemical industries for synthetic sodium nitrate.

CHAPTER V

CONCLUSIONS

CHILEAN VS. SYNTHETIC NITROGEN

It was mentioned in Chapter II that from a predominant world position as a source of nitrogen, Chile had sunk to a decidedly minor position by 1931. The world capacity of fixed and by-product nitrogen in that year had reached the enormous total of 3,300,000 tons, whereas the total actual consumption for the year 1930–31 was placed at only 1,760,-000 tons. There is, therefore, at the present time a sufficient synthetic nitrogen capacity to take care of almost double the amount consumed. Under normal circumstances survival of the Chilean industry would be achieved on the basis of production costs. Chilean nitrate has now been driven to struggle not for supremacy but for its very existence.

It is argued by many that a product that just has to be picked off the ground will always be able to crowd out one that is produced artificially. The problem, however, is not so simple as that. It has been shown in Chapter II that the separation of the nitrate from the caliche is a manufacturing operation. The Chilean nitrate industry is an industry not different, except in method, from the pig iron industry. In both cases the mined ore has to be submitted to a series of operations before the desired product is obtained. Machinery requiring large capital investment is needed in one case as well as in the other and capital charges must therefore be figured in production costs in both cases. These capital charges, as already shown, have proved too heavy for the nitrate industry to bear.

The Chilean industry is furthermore confronted by two severe handicaps. The first is its great distance from consuming centers which necessitates important additions to ton costs for transportation. The second is the determination of nations large and small not to be faced again with the conditions that developed during the War and to protect at all costs their nitrogen industry on which they will have to depend in case of a blockade in which they might be directly or indirectly involved. This is by far the more serious of the two. The raid of von Spee and the submarine campaign are still remembered. Furthermore, the increasing effectiveness of the bombing plane makes it evident that a blockade will be carried out far more thoroughly in a future war than was thought possible in the World War.

The cost of producing Chilean nitrate by the old Shanks process was carefully studied by H. Foster Bain and H. S. Mulliken of our Department of Commerce in 1924. They reached a figure of $16.72 per short ton, without the Government tax. Adding the $10 of this tax,* the cost in Chilean port was $26.72. The shipping charges, insurance, commissions, financing of shipment, etc., added $8.80 to this amount, making the cost at an American port $35.52. At that time nitrate was selling in the United States at $50.40 a ton, leaving a good margin of profit. At present quotations, however, Shanks nitrate would sell at a loss of $14.50 a ton and even if the Government tax were eliminated, it would be selling at a loss of $4.50 a ton.

If, as the Cosach organizers boasted to the Chilean Congress in 1930, the cost of production would be reduced by the Guggenheim process $8.00 per ton, making the cost delivered say $27.00, there is still a wide margin of loss before the nitrate can compete with other nitrogenous fertilizers. The "abolition" of the Government tax is in reality only a change of name. The Chilean Government fully expects to have its former income to continue, if not as a tax, as dividends on the stock it has received. The tremendous overhead of the Guggenheim plants has set at naught the claims of economy in mechanical production and the lowered con-

*The tax of $12 a metric ton is here figured on the basis of the short ton and taking into account the prevailing rate of exchange at the time.

sumption of Chilean nitrate has thrown out of gear all the calculations based on a production of 2,600,000 tons of nitrate a year.

The abandonment of the gold standard by Chile in May, 1932 will only temporarily work in favor of her nitrate exports. Her labor costs will be cheaper, at least for a while, since the workmen will be paid in depreciated currency and the product of their labor will be sold in either gold standard countries or countries where currencies are not very far away from their former gold value. This would work to the advantage of the Shanks process plants where labor is more plentifully employed than in the Guggenheim process where machines do the work. Balancing this advantage, however, will be the higher prices in terms of national currency that will have to be paid for materials needed in the exploitation of the caliche fields such as petroleum products, bagging material and replacement machinery all of which will have to be imported. From this source no great increase in competition need be expected by the synthetic nitrogen industry.

More serious would be a proposed capital readjustment through which bondholders would receive stock instead of bonds. The capital charges for retirement of the bonds which would be thereby eliminated would materially decrease the ton cost but even under those circumstances provision will have to be made for depreciation of machinery which would be a sizeable item on such a large investment.

The latest proposition for the reorganization of the Cosach contemplates the formation of a new corporation with $65,000,000 common stock and $132,000,000 bonded indebtedness; $443,218,750 of bonds, preferred and common stock outstanding are to be cancelled. In this amount would be included the $40,000,000 of bonds given by the Cosach to the Chilean Government in lieu of the export tax as well as the $187,000,000 common stock held by the Chilean Government. (See Appendix IV). In exchange the Cosach offers to Chile either a share of the profits or $35,000,000 of new common stock, to be issued in addition to the $65,-000,000 contemplated.

How the Cosach expects to make any profits on its stock at present prices, is difficult to see. The interest charges on the new bonds at 6 per cent would be $7,920,000 and with a conservative sinking fund provision of 2 per cent this overhead would become $10,560,000. On an export of 1,000,000 tons this would add $10.56 to the price of $16.00 a ton at consumer's port, making it $26.56 per ton. The exports for 1931 were considerably less than 1,000,000 tons and the exports for the first six months of 1932 were 218,000 tons, so that by selling nitrate at the present price of $21.00 a ton in the United States, a loss of at least $6.00 a ton is being incurred by the Cosach and probably double that amount if the overhead be figured on the exports for January-July, 1932. That the Chilean Government would accept the offer of the Cosach as outlined, is out of the question. The Government must have some income from its chief industry and the plan that will finally evolve will increase rather than decrease these overhead charges.

In the meantime stocks of nitrate continue to accumulate.

The presence of these unsold stocks constitutes a threat that must not be minimized. It is estimated that there are 2,000,000 tons of nitrate in storage in Chile and close to 1,000,000 tons in other countries, chiefly in England, which has been for a great many years the distributing point for continental Europe. In this country the stocks amounted to 350,000 tons in February, 1932 and had been only slightly lowered by June of the same year. As already mentioned, the only market of any consequence, besides Egypt, which has no duty or embargo on Chilean nitrate, is the American market and our industry will have hanging over it for some time to come the threat of these 3,000,000 tons of nitrate which may at any time be "dumped" for what they may bring. The only safeguards against reckless dumping at the present moment are first the inability of the market to absorb any such amounts of nitrate at any price and next the bank loans that have been made to the Cosach on this stored nitrate as security. These loans involve considerable amounts. The Chilean branch of the Anglo-South American

Bank has recently had to be relieved of the burden of frozen assets of these nitrate loans by a syndicate which included the Bank of England. These frozen nitrate assets amounted to £7,500,000.

According to Associated Press despatches, the Edwards and Co. Bank of Santiago, Chile, has recently through court proceedings placed an embargo on 150,000 tons of nitrate stored in northern Chilean ports and belonging to the Cosach, to satisfy a loan of $1,300,000 made to that company. This would indicate a loan of $8.66 per ton in Chile. If this Bank should decide to liquidate this loan, it could place that nitrate in an American port substantially below the market price, incur no loss and even make a profit. This particular amount of nitrate is not considerable but it serves to illustrate what may have to be faced in the not distant future.

The Chilean industry's only salvation lies in the destruction of our fixed nitrogen industry and we may expect every effort in that direction by outright "dumping" in our market.

With the 3,000,000 tons of stocks shut out from all countries except our own and Egypt, which takes only about 200,000 tons a year, this dumping could proceed long enough to spell disaster to our industry.

Unless such destruction be achieved and Chile then again be in control and able to raise prices to profitable levels, we may consider the Chilean nitrate industry as an obsolescent one, which can continue to exist only by toleration and the influence exercised on the synthetic producers by the banking houses deeply involved in Chilean affairs. Eventually it should join the museum of discarded industries which have not been able to meet the modern conditions created by synthetic chemistry. Examples are not lacking.

For centuries the root of the madder plant had furnished the very valuable dyestuff, alizarin. Until the last quarter of the nineteenth century madder plantations flourished in France, Italy and Holland, but when the English chemist, W. H. Perkin, finally synthesised alizarin from coal tar derivatives, the plantations gradually disappeared and have now vanished altogether.

Forty years ago the growing of the indigo plant for the blue dye obtained from it was one of the outstanding industries of India, but with the advent of synthetic indigo, it has disappeared, though it struggled valiantly for a while.

CHILEAN NITRATE PROPAGANDA

Curiously enough the same weapon, propaganda, and the same type of propaganda, was utilized by the expiring indigo industry as is being extensively used by the Chilean interests in our South Atlantic States where Chilean nitrate finds its best market. "The synthetic indigo is too pure and concentrated to give satisfactory practical results", said the indigo planters. "The natural nitrate is better than the synthetic for it has certain impurities that help the growing of the plants", the nitrate producers say. This in the face of categorical denials of the chief chemist of the Department of Agriculture that any such effect has been shown to exist.*

This propaganda has gone so far as to suggest that during the War, German explosives did not give as good results as the Allies' because they were made with synthetic nitrate, whereas the Allies used the God-given product of Chile. The Allied soldiers in the trenches would have fervently hoped that that might have been the case.

The extent and power of this propaganda has been considerable. "Few commodities of world trade", wrote Harry A. Curtis of the Department of Commerce in 1926, "have been so widely and consistently advertised as Chilean nitrate. As early as 1897 the Chilean Government set aside £20,000 for nitrate propaganda on the stipulation that the producers would contribute £12,000. Later the Government's grant was raised to £40,000 but the producers were then spending nearly twice this amount on educational campaigns. In 1922-23 the total spent in this way was about £212,575, of which the Chilean Government contributed £40,375. Of this total about £79,000 or 37 per cent, was spent on nitrate propaganda in the United States."

*See Appendix III.

But with increasing intelligent use of fertilizers and especially now that the depression in prices of agricultural products compels the farmer to look closely to production costs, the effect of this propaganda will gradually fade out.

HANDICAPS OF NITROGEN PRODUCERS IN THE UNITED STATES

On fair basis of competition the synthetic nitrogen industry can more than cope with the Chilean industry. The synthetic industry has lowered the cost of nitrogen to the farmer beyond what he might have reasonably hoped ten years ago. It is against the possibility of the assault of unfair competition by a powerful organization that European countries have set up barriers against Chilean imports and it behooves us to be on the alert lest the $161,000,000 invested by the Government and the American synthetic nitrogen industry be imperiled by any such assault.

The American industry is at a distinct disadvantage, for it cannot organize as its foreign competitors do on account of antitrust law regulations and each unit must fight by itself against a common enemy.

Protective action by our Government takes much time and becomes effective usually after much harm has been done. The prompt and adequate cooperation between European Governments and their industries is beyond our conception. When in July, 1931, a new nitrogen cartel was in process of formation at Lucerne in Switzerland, and the exorbitant demands of the Chileans made it apparent that no agreement could be reached and while the delegates were still assembled, the German Government issued a decree on July 15th placing a duty of $29 a ton on imports of Chilean nitrate. Other European countries followed in rapid succession either with additional duties or requirements of special import licenses, Poland on July 22nd, Czechoslovakia on August 6th, Belgium on August 20th and Italy on August 21st. France had already similarly protected herself in May of the same year. (See Appendix VI.)

On the other hand the American producers of both synthetic and coke oven ammonia find all markets closed to them by barriers of duties and licenses and must face at home the competition of the foreign producer who may find it cheaper after his home market has been supplied to dump his product here rather than pay storage charges. Not only have Holland, Germany, Belgium, England and Poland been heavy shippers of ammonium sulphate to this country to an unprecedented extent in 1932 but Japan* also has been shipping ammonium sulphate to the Pacific coast and compelled the partial shutting down of the Shell Chemical Company's plant at Pittsburg, California, which was producing ammonium sulphate synthetically. The lowering of the nitrogen prices from this dumped sulphate involves the entire industry, both the synthetic nitrate and the coke oven sulphate.

It is not very difficult to see that there is a world campaign directed against the elimination of our nitrogen industry. The present losses incurred by the nitrogen cartel, however, are to be considered in the nature of a loan, payment of which with exorbitant interest will be duly exacted when our industry will have been compelled to shut down and scrap its plants.

It should be realized by the farmers and our political leaders that a period of extremely low nitrogen prices induced by unchecked foreign dumping will have to be paid for dearly once our nitrogen industry would have been driven to bankruptcy and its workers thrown out of employment. The old monopoly would again be in control and we may have to pray for another gold reserve episode, to secure reasonable prices.

FOREIGN MONOPOLIES

The United States has always been the promised land for cartels and monopolies. The rubber, coffee, potash, nitrate and many other monopolies have been directed chiefly at the control or exploitation of our home market.

*See Appendix VIII.

Article 5 of the nitrogen cartel of 1930 provided that "The United States be excepted from the application of this convention as being considered the exclusive market of Chile". We can visualize signs of "Private Property, Keep Off" placed at our ports of entry by the Chilean nitrate monopoly.

Many of these cartels and monopolies are now things of the past but during the post-war decade they became sufficiently troublesome to draw the attention of our legislators and of our Department of Commerce then under Mr. Herbert Hoover. "The situation is one of great gravity", wrote Mr. Hoover in 1926, "not only to ourselves but to the world as a whole. The issue is much broader than the price of a particular commodity which may be at the moment vividly in the public mind; it involves the whole policy that our country shall pursue toward a comparatively new and growing menace in international commerce and relations. This development not only threatens the same progress of the world but involves great dangers to international good will. . . . It has been said that, given time, all these things will remedy themselves by inexorable economic law. It may be so, but in the meantime we may pay out billions while the law is in process of operating. And with governmental controls these inexorable results can be delayed over many years." "Inexorable economic law" has worked to the detriment of many of these cartels but there are still some of more recent origin against which we have as yet to contend. Though the world nitrogen cartels have all been fiascos, the understanding between the British Chemical Trust and the German Chemical Trust is still in force as evidenced by the annual report of the Imperial Chemical Industries, Ltd. (See Appendix V.)

The Secretary of Commerce further unerringly pointed to the remedy against the intolerable conditions: "In certain commodities we can find relief through synthetic chemistry", he wrote.

We *have* found relief through synthetic chemistry for our nitrogen situation and a bounteous nature has freed us from

the exactions of the potash monopoly, for within the last
year the mines of Carlsbad, New Mexico, have begun shipments of potash salts and within a short time should supply
all our requirements. Of phosphate we have been one of the
world's leading producers for many years. We are now,
therefore, entirely self-contained for all our fertilizer demands
and independent of any nation for our military requirements
of nitrogen but that independence will not last long if we
allow ourselves to fall again into the hands of the monopolies
and cartels and again have to pay millions, if not billions,
before the "inexorable economic law" be again in process of
operating.

THE END

APPENDIX I

SHORT BIBLIOGRAPHY OF WORKS ON NITROGEN

FIXED NITROGEN, edited by Harry A. Curtis, American Chemical Society Monograph No. 59. The Chemical Catalog Co., 419 Fourth Avenue, New York, 1932.
> The most thorough and authoritative publication on this subject. Technical.

FIXATION OF ATMOSPHERIC NITROGEN, by F. A. Ernst. Industrial Chemical Monographs, D. Van Nostrand Company, 8 Warren Street, New York, 1928.
> A very good treatise on the subject. Semi-technical in language.

NITRIC ACID AND NITRATES, by Allin G. Cottrell, Gurney and Jackson, London, 1923.
> Contains an excellent chapter on the Chilean nitrate industry, limited, however, to the old processes before the appearance of the Guggenheim process.

GOVERNMENT PUBLICATIONS

AMERICAN INDUSTRY IN THE WAR. A Report of the War Industries Board, by Bernard M. Baruch, Washington, Government Printing Office, 1921.
> Of historical interest.

REPORT ON THE FIXATION AND UTILIZATION OF NITROGEN. Nitrate Division, Ordnance Department and Fixed Nitrogen Laboratory, Washington, Government Printing Office, 1922.
> Historical.

United States Department of Commerce Trade Information Bulletin No. 170. Nitrogen Survey. Part I. THE COST OF CHILEAN NITRATE, by H. Foster Bain and H. S. Mulliken. Washington, Government Printing Office, 1924.

The best and most thorough survey of the production cost of the Shanks process.

United States Department of Commerce Trade Information Bulletin, No. 226, Part II. GENERAL REVIEW OF THE NITROGEN SITUATION IN THE UNITED STATES, by Harry A. Curtis. Washington, Government Printing Office, 1924.

Contains very interesting data on Chilean industry. Mostly historical now.

United States Department of Commerce Bureau of Foreign and Domestic Commerce. FOREIGN COMBINATIONS TO CONTROL PRICES OF RAW MATERIALS. Statements by Herbert Hoover, Secretary of Commerce, and other Officers of the Department of Commerce. Trade Information Bulletin No. 385. Washington, Government Printing Office, 1926.

An excellent picture of conditions as they existed and as they might appear again.

United States Department of Agriculture. Circular No. 129, January, 1931. SURVEY OF THE FERTILIZER INDUSTRY, by P. E. Howard, United States Government Printing Office.

A very thorough review with interesting statistics regarding the nitrogen situation.

AMERICAN FERTILIZERS, Miscellaneous Publication No. 143,
United States Department of Agriculture, by P. E.
Howard, Fixed Nitrogen Research Laboratory. Wash-
ington, United States Government Printing Office, 1932.
An excellent non-technical review of actual conditions.

Most of the articles in technical publications are
thought beyond the scope of this little volume. The
following articles by Chas. J. Brand, Executive Secretary
and Treasurer of the National Fertilizer Association, are
written in non-technical style and are filled with
valuable information.

BY-PRODUCT NITROGEN AND THE FERTILIZER INDUSTRY.
Proceeding of the Second International Conference on
Bituminous Coal, 1928.

RECENT DEVELOPMENTS IN THE FERTILIZER INDUSTRY. Proceedings of the Sixth Annual Convention of the National
Fertilizer Association, Washington, D. C., 1930.

NITROGEN AND THE FERTILIZER INDUSTRY. Journal of the
Franklin Institute, Vol. 207, May, 1929.

A very complete bibliography on nitrogen is on file at
the Fixed Nitrogen Research Laboratory in Washington,
D. C. Bibliographies are also appended to FIXED
NITROGEN, by Harry A. Curtis, and to THE FIXATION
OF ATMOSPHERIC NITROGEN, by F. A. Ernst.

APPENDIX II

WORLD PRODUCTION AND CONSUMPTION OF FIXED NITROGEN

The present world nitrogen-producing capacity is estimated at 3,000,000 metric tons, exclusive of Chilean. Actual production during the year ended June 30, 1931, was estimated at 1,694,288 metric tons, a decrease of about 23 per cent from the previous fiscal year. The total consumption fell 329,492 tons, or 17 per cent.

The following figures in metric tons, reprinted from World Trade Notes on Chemical and Allied Products, issued February 8, 1932, by the Chemical Division of the Department of Commerce, are offered as fair estimates, but strict accuracy is not claimed for them.

WORLD PRODUCTION AND CONSUMPTION OF PURE NITROGEN

	1926-27 Tons	1927-28 Tons	1928-29 Tons	1929-30 Tons	1930-31 Tons
Sulfate of Ammonia					
By-Product.............	328,200	368,000	376,000	424,440	359,594
Synthetic...............	300,000	367,000	485,000	442,100	349,087
	628,200	735,000	861,000	866,540	708,681
Cyanamide	180,000	204,000	210,000	263,800	200,932
Nitrate of Lime............	81,000	105,000	136,000	130,500	110,585
Other Forms of Nitrogen(a)					
Synthetic................	183,400	236,000	365,000	427,300	393,150
By-Product.............	50,300	54,000	51,000	51,400	30,940
Chile Nitrate...............	199,600	390,000	490,000	464,000	250,000
TOTAL PRODUCTION..	1,322,500	1,724,000	2,113,000	2,203,540	1,694,288
Consumption					
Manufactured Nitrogen....	1,091,177	1,249,669	1,452,630	1,586,904	1,377,005
Chile Nitrate............	275,158	392,722	419,450	363,893	244,300
TOTAL CONSUMPTION.	1,366,335	1,642,391	1,872,080	1,950,797	1,621,305
Approximate Agricultural					
Consumption............	1,200,000	1,490,000	1,684,000	1,750,000	1,455,000

(a)Including ammonia products used for industrial purposes and ammonia in mixed fertilizers.

NOTE.—Fertilizers are included under the final form as sold, so that, for example, cyanamide if converted into sulfate of ammonia is included under synthetic sulfate of ammonia, or, if into ammophos, is included under other synthetic nitrogen.

From Industrial and Engineering Chemistry, News Section, March, 1932.

APPENDIX III

THE UNITED STATES DEPARTMENT OF AGRICULTURE SPEAKS REGARDING NATURAL AND SYNTHETIC NITRATE OF SODA

"My attention has been called to claims that are being made with reference to the relative values of different forms of nitrogen fertilizers, some of which are apparently being repeated by extension workers. In order to be certain whether there was basis in fact for such claims of superiority, I made inquiry of Dr. H. G. Knight, Chief of the Bureau of Chemistry and Soils of this Department, from whom I now have the following statement:

'We have looked over the literature and so far as we have been able to find there is no conclusive experimental evidence to show that the natural nitrates are superior to the synthetic forms. In the absence of conclusive experimental evidence this Bureau can see no justification for recommending one form in preference to the other provided they are both in satisfactory mechanical condition.'

"In view of Dr. Knight's statement, I feel that extension workers should refrain from recommending one form of nitrogen fertilizer over another except as such recommendations are based on specific facts."

From a letter written by Dr. C. W. Warburton, Director of the Extension Service, U. S. Dept. of Agriculture, to State Directors of Extension, March 20, 1931.

The Fertilizer Review, March, 1931.

APPENDIX IV.

The Cosach indebtedness. Extract from a public statement of Senor Luis Izquierdo, Minister of the Interior of the Republic of Chile, published in the Chilean press on May 29, 1932.*

VI.

When the Compañia de Salitre de Chile was organized, it took over obligations of various kinds representing a total expressed by an astronomical figure. Naturally, there were two kinds of obligations, preferred or privileged—prior secured bonds and secured bonds—which have as guaranty the sum of sixty pesos per metric ton levied by the Chilean customs which sum is turned over to the bankers. This category of bonds includes $40,140,000 turned over to the Government in lieu of its yearly income, $8,565,000 debt to the Compañia Salitrera de Tocopilla, $2,300,000 to the Nitrates Agencies, $4,122,000 to Grace and Co. in payment for the Compañia de Tarapacá y Tocopilla, $2,918,000 to various nitrate companies, Compañia Salitrera y Comercial de Tarapacá, belonging to the firm of Gildemeister and Co., Compañia Salitrera de Taltal, La Granja and Nueva Castilla belonging to various owners. In this privileged category belong also the bonds floated in the United States for a total of $19,000,000 and in England for £3,000,000 for the immediate cash requirements of the company and to pay the State Treasury. Finally there is included the much discussed debt of $27,144,000 owed by the Anglo Chilean to the firm of Guggenheim which the Cosach acknowledged as its own. Total $104,210,000 and £3,000,000.

The loans secured by mortgages on the property of companies absorbed by the Cosach and their subsidiaries, amount to £6,483,605 and $46,021,000, and the miscellaneous debts which the Cosach assumed amount to £12,172,737 and $8,092,562.

Among the creditors are to be found the great European banking houses of Baring Bros. and Co., Morgan, Grenfell

*Translated by the author from *El Diario Ilustrado*, Santiago, Chile, May 29, 1932.

& Co., N. M. Rothschild & Sons, J. Henry Schroeder & Co., Mendelsohn & Co., Credit Suisse, Anglo-South American Bank, and others of minor importance. Among the United States creditors are the firms of Guggenheim, W. R. Grace and Co., Guaranty Trust Co., J. P. Morgan & Co., Bankers Trust Co., Central Hanover Bank, National City Bank. In addition there are among us creditor banks which will surely have our backing.

THE REORGANIZATION OF THE COSACH
From the "El Mercurio" Santiago, Chile, August 26, 1932*

PRESENT LIABILITIES	PROPOSED REORGANIZATION			TO BE CANCELLED
	Debentures	Mortgage Bonds	Common Stock	
$49,000,000 prior secured bonds	$49,000,000	....	....	....
$68,000,000 junior secured bonds	....	$14,000,000	$14,000,000	$40,000,000 (a)
$5,500,000 debts assumed by Cosach	....	1,375,000	2,750,000	1,375,000
$63,000,000 bonds of Lautaro & Anglo-Chilean	....	47,625,000	15,875,000	....
$40,000,000 debts of subsidiaries	....	20,000,000	10,000,000	10,000,000
$40,000,000 Lautaro pfd. and $55,000,000 Cosach pfd.	....	....	21,000,000	74,000,000
$66,250,000 common Cosach issued to Guggenheim	....	....	....	66,250,000
$66,250,000 Cosach common issued to others	....	....	1,656,250	64,593,750
$187,000,000 Cosach common issued to Chilean Govern.	....	....	....	187,000,000
Totals	$49,000,000	$83,000,000	$65,281,250	$443,218,750

(a) Bonds given to the Chilean Government in lieu of export tax.

*Translated by the author.

APPENDIX V.

Extract from the annual report of "Imperial Chemical Industries, Ltd." as published in the *London Times*, April 15, 1932.

NITROGEN

We also participated in another international agreement which, unfortunately, was of but short duration. The International Nitrogen Convention, in which numerous European manufacturers of synthetic nitrogen joined, between which and the Chilean producers of natural nitrate of soda there were marketing and financial relations, was admittedly of a temporary nature, pending, it was hoped, the conclusion of a lasting agreement. During its short life the convention did much to assist in orderly marketing, apart from its substantial contribution towards regulating production to consumption. Negotiations last summer for the continuance of the convention unfortunately broke down. *The close cooperation which we had already established with the German synthetic nitrogen producers has not been affected.** During the period of unrestricted competition through which the nitrogen industry is now passing these arrangements are of material assistance to each party. We both stand ready to consider and to take an active part in bringing into operation any equitable scheme for restoring order in the world's nitrogen industry, which, while still satisfying national aspirations, will enable plants to be run on a stable international basis, and fertilizers to be sold at a price holding a fair balance between producer and consumer.

In foreign markets the outlook for fertilizers is obscure. Only as agricultural conditions improve can any substantial revival of demand be expected. At home the picture is more encouraging. The nation is now appreciating that an increase in home food production is one of the pressing problems before the country, both as regards the prosperity of agriculture itself and the ultimate stability of the nation.

Italics are the author's.

APPENDIX VI.

THE FOLLOWING INFORMATION RELATIVE TO TARIFF RATES, LICENSES AND OTHER RESTRICTIONS ON THE IMPORTATION OF NITROGEN PRODUCTS INTO GERMANY, FRANCE, ITALY, POLAND, CZECHOSLOVAKIA, JAPAN, BELGIUM, UNITED KINGDOM AND CANADA WAS FURNISHED BY THE UNITED STATES DEPARTMENT OF COMMERCE.

CZECHOSLOVAKIA

Assistant Trade Commissioner Sam. E. Woods, Prague, October 23.

Import Licenses Required for Certain Nitrogenous Products

By a ministerial decree of July 31, published in the Official Gazette of August 4 and effective August 6, 1931, the importation into Czechoslovakia of the following nitrogenous products were made subject to license:

Tariff Item	*Commodity*
597 and ex 652 . . .	Ammonia liquor, concentrated and nonconcentrated.
ex 598b	Nitric acid.
ex 599a	Nitrate of soda and nitrate of lime.
ex 599g	Ammonium sulphate.
600m	Calcium cyanamide
ex 622	Nitrogenous fertilizers and compound nitrogenous fertilizers.

No fee is collected for the issue of licenses for any of the above products.

It is reported that the above is intended primarily as a precautionary measure, and so far no requests for import licenses have been refused.

FRANCE

Cablegram from Acting Commercial Attache Daniel J. Reagan, May 11.

Import Licenses Required for Certain Fertilizers.

The importation of certain nitrogenous fertilizers into France has been temporarily subjected to the requirement of import licenses, by a decree of May 5, published in the Journal Officiel for May 7, and effective May 8, 1931.

The products for the importation of which licenses will be required include: Ammonium sulphate, mixed or not with ammonium nitrate; natural and synthetic sodium nitrate; calcium nitrate; and calcium cyanamide. Import licenses are to be issued under the direction of the Minister of Agriculture, with the approval of the Minister of Finance. Applications for licenses are to be made by importers, on standard forms in triplicate, to the Direction Generale de l'Agriculture at the Ministry of Agriculture, which will transmit the request to the customs administration at the Ministry of Finance.

Merchandise proved to have been shipped for France before May 7, 1931, is not affected by the decree, and will be admitted without import licenses.

GERMANY

Cablegrams from Commercial Attache H. Lawrence Groves, Berlin, July 17 and 21.

Increased Import Duties on Nitrogenous Fertilizers and Chemicals.

Increased import duties ranging from 8 to 24 Reichsmarks per 100 kilos were decreed by the German Government on nitrogenous fertilizers and chemicals on July 13, and effective from July 15, 1931.

The following are the products affected, with the new duties in Reichsmarks per 100 kilos (old rates in parenthesis):

Item 271, ammoniacal liquor (gas liquor) or liquid ammonia (free), 8; item 274, nitric acid (free), 12; item 268, carbonate of ammonia (hartshorn salts) (free), 20; item 302, nitrate of ammonia (ammonia saltpeter), not imported in shells or capsules (free), 24; item 303, nitrate of soda (Chile saltpeter) (free), 12; item ex 304a, nitrate of potash (free), 24; 304b, ammonium chloride, ammonium sulphate, calcium nitrate, also with an ammonium content of not over 8 per cent, urea, calcium cyanamide (all formerly free under 317v), 12.

Item 362a, fertilizer containing phosphorus, which has been treated with acid (superphosphates), also when mixed with other substances: mixed with nitrogenous substances (0.50), 12; others under this classification remaining unchanged at 0.50; item 362b (new item), nitrogenous fertilizers not specified or indicated, 12; item 379, liquefied gases; anhydrous ammonia in tank cars or vehicles arranged for the transportation of liquefied gases in bulk (8), 12; other liquefied gases remain unchanged at 8.

Note to items 359 to 362a: Dutiable substances intended for uses as fertilizers which are not specified in items 359 to 362a, may be allowed duty-free entry under guaranty that they will be used as fertilizers; this does not apply to items 286, 302 (1), 303-304a (1), 304b, 317d, and 362b.

GERMANY

Commercial Attache H. Lawrence Groves, Berlin, August 19.

Special Licenses Required for Importation of Certain Fertilizers.

Effective August 18, 1931, special permits will be required for the importation into Germany of ammonium chloride, ammonium sulphate, urea, and ammonium, sodium, and calcium nitrates, as well as other fertilizers containing nitrogen, according to a decree published in the Reichsanzeiger (Government Bulletin) of August 17, 1931.

It is understood that this measure has been taken in order to render more effective the protective duties on the above products, which came into force on July 15, 1931.

POLAND

Radiogram from Commercial Attache Clayton M. Lane, Warsaw, July 27.

Import Restriction Placed on Chemical Fertilizers.

A Polish decree established July 22, 1931, prohibits the importation of the following products, except under authorization from the ministry of commerce:

Ammonium nitrate, ammonium sulphate, Chilean salt-peter, sodium nitrate, calcium nitrate, calcium cyanamide, and compounds of these products.

ITALY

Radiogram from Assistant Commercial Attache A. A. Osborne, Rome, August 22.

Import Duties Increased on Nitrogen Derivatives and Fertilizer Materials.

An Italian decree, effective August 21, 1931, increased the rates of duty of the general tariff on various nitrogen deriva-tives and fertilizer materials.

The following table gives the old and new general rates and existing conventional rates in paper lire per 100 kilos. The conventional rates apply on imports of such products from the United States and certain other countries. Products for which conventional rates have not been established are dutiable under the new general rates.

Tariff Item No.	Product	Old General Rates	New General Rates	Conven-tional Rates
		Paper lire per 100 kilos	*Paper lire per 100 kilos*	*Paper lire per 100 kilos*
672-i	Nitric acid............................	14.70	55.00	11.00
676-b	Ammonia in solution...................	18.35	55.00	18.35
676-bis	Concentrated gas plant ammonia liquors..	Free	55.00	None
715-b	Crude sodium nitrate, including synthetic calcium nitrate......................	Free	55.00	None
715-b-3	Cyanamide...........................	11.00	55.00	11.00
715-b-4	Ammonium sulphate...................	3.65	55.00	None
676-a	Compressed ammonia..................	44.00	110.00	44.00
689-a	Ammonium nitrate....................	29.40	110.00	None
689-f	Potassium nitrate.....................	11.00	110.00	7.35
686-a	Ammonium chloride....................	44.00	75.00	None
690	Potassium and sodium nitrates..........	44.00	75.00	36.70
689-g	Refined sodium nitrate.................	11.00	75.00	None
715-d	Mixed nitrogen fertilizers..............	3.65	75.00	None
715-E	Unspecified nitrogen fertilizers..........	Free	75.00	None
680-a	Ammonium carbonate..................	52.80	90.00	44.00
715-b-5	Ammonium nitrate, impure.............	3.65	100.00	None

(Existing conventional rates apply also to imports from Belgium, France, Germany, and Chile.)

Annual quota of Sodium Nitrate admitted Duty Free.

An annual quota of sodium nitrate, fixed each year in accordance with the needs of the country, is admitted into Italy duty-free. For 1931 this quota was 60,000 tons.

The quota for 1932 has been fixed at 20,000 tons, 17,000 tons of which was allocated to Chile and 2,000 to Germany; the remaining 1,000 tons being divided among other countries.

BELGIUM

Economic and Trade Notes No. 38.
Submitted by Assistant Commercial Attache Leigh W. Hunt, Brussels, August 21.

Regulation of Import and Transit of Nitrogen Products.

The "Moniteur Belge" of August 20, 1931, publishes the following royal decree regulating the importation and transit of nitrogen products in Belgium:

Article 1.   In order to safeguard the vital interest of the country, the importation and transit of all nitrogen products are temporarily subjected to the obtaining of an authorization from the Ministry of Industry and Labor, which ministry will establish the nomenclature of the products concerned.

Article 2.   The Ministry of Industry and Labor, the Ministry of Finance, and the Ministry of Agriculture will be charged, insofar as each is concerned, with the execution of the present decree, which will enter into force on the day of its publication in the "Moniteur Belge."

Following the publication of the above royal decree, the ministerial decree quoted below has appeared in the "Moniteur Belge" of August 21:

Article 1.   Are subjected to the obtaining of an authorization to be delivered by the Ministry of Industry and Labor the importation and transit of:-

(a) Nitrogen fertilizers such as: natural nitrate of soda or chemical nitrate of soda; nitrate of ammonia; nitrate of lime; kalkonitre; kalkammon-saltpeter.

(b) Ammonia fertilizers such as: sulphate of ammonia, chlorate of ammonia.

(c) Starch fertilizers such as: cyanamide, urea.

(d) Mixed fertilizers such as: phosphate and superphosphate of ammonia; sulphonitrate of ammonia; potassium nitrate; nitrophoska; nitrophosphorite.

(e) The following nitrogen products: anhydrous ammonia; ammonia solution of all concentrations; nitric acid of all concentrations; sulphonitric acids; sulphate of ammonia refined or commercially pure; nitrate of soda pure or refined; nitrate of potassium refined; ammonia carbonates; ammonium chlorate; pure urea.

JAPAN

Statement of rates of import duty of February 9.

		Rate of Duty Ad Valorem
189	Sulphate of ammonium:	
	1. Refined	20%
	2. Other	Free

Regulations on Import and Export Permits for Sulphate of Ammonia.

Article 1.   Sulphate of ammonia is the commodity covered by these regulations.   Crude sulphate of ammonia is that which contains over 80 per cent and upon which these regulations apply.

Article 2.   A permit from the Ministries of Agriculture and Forestry and Commerce and Industry must be obtained by any one intending to import or export sulphate of ammonia.

Article 3.   In order to obtain an import license for sulphate of ammonia the following facts must be stated on the application:

(a) The quantity to be imported
(b) Port of shipment and port of importation
(c) Time of shipment and time of import

(d) Place of manufacture

(e) Those persons who at present have sales licenses for fertilizer must state the name on the license and the fertilizer covered thereby, the guaranteed analysis, the name of the officer granting the license and date of license.

Article 4.   If the importation of sulphate of ammonia as applied for is considered necessary the Ministries of the Departments concerned will publish the date of application for the notification of the public.

Article 5.   Any person desiring to export sulphate of ammonia shall apply to the Ministries of Agriculture and Forestry and Commerce and Industry, stating the following tems:

(a) quantity to be exported

(b) ports to which the commodity is to be exported

(c) loading ports

(d) the period desired during which exports will be made

(e) the names of the manufacturers or companies desiring export.

Article 6.   Any person who has obtained an export or import license may not alter in any degree the terms thereof without permission from the aforementioned Departments.

Article 7.   The Ministers of the Departments mentioned previously in granting licenses for the import or export of sulphate of ammonia shall specify the date of shipment and import or export period.   If the importing or exporting is not done during the specified period the licenses become void.   In case it is impossible for unavoidable reasons to fulfill the terms of the license an extension may be made by the Ministers in charge.

Article 8.   Importers of sulphate of ammonia who have obtained licenses shall report to the Ministries the quantity, port from which shipped, name of steamer, and shipping date.

Article 9.   Importers or exporters of sulphate of ammonia must report to the Ministries mentioned the amounts imported or exported and the import or export date without delay.

Article 10.   Manufacturers of sulphate of ammonia shall report to the Ministries of Commerce and Industry and Agriculture and Forestry their estimated monthly manufacturing quantities for the period of August 1st to July 31st of the next year on or before July 31st.   In case changes are made in their estimates during the year these changes must be reported to the authorities.   Sulphate of ammonia manufacturers will report their monthly production to the Ministries before the 10th of the following month.

Article 11.   Any person intending to transship sulphate of ammonia during the period August 1st to July 1st shall report the estimated quantity which he will transship before July 31st of each year.

Article 12.   The rules apply to exporters of sulphate of ammonia also.

Article 13.   Transshippers of sulphate of ammonia must report without delay to the Ministries mentioned the following facts:

    (a) quantity transshipped

    (b) manufacturers' names

  or, if these are unknown, places of production

    (c) shipping ports, ports of destination

    (d) date of transshipment.

Article 14.   Applications for import or export licenses shall be made out in duplicate and submitted to the two aforementioned Ministries.

Article 15.   Any person who violates the regulations of this act shall be punished with not less than three months' penal servitude or less than ¥100 fine.

    (a) Any person importing or exporting sulphate of ammonia without permit is liable to the punishment mentioned above.

(b) Any person who transships or transships in excess of the amount indicated on his permit is also liable to punishment.

(c) Any person who does not make a report of shipments as required by this act is also liable to punishment.

SUPPLEMENTARY REGULATIONS

The regulations of this act will be in effect on the date of promulgation, *i. e.*, December 8th, 1931.

Persons importing or transshipping sulphate of ammonia will not require permits until January 15th, 1932.

Sulphate of ammonia in bonded warehouses at the time of the promulgation of this act or sulphate of ammonia which has been contracted for and will be shipped to Japan before January 15th, 1932, if reported within 30 days after this regulation became effective, will not be covered by this act.

UNITED KINGDOM

Sodium Nitrate and Ammonium Sulphate

Tariff No.		General Tariff ad valorem	British Preferential Tariff
X. 22	Sodium Nitrate............	20%	Free
	Sulphate of Ammonia.......	20%	Free

The rates of the General Tariff apply to shipments from all non-British sources. Duty imposed by Order No. 1, under Import Duties Act, 1932—effective April 26, 1932.

In its agreements made at the time of the Imperial Conference at Ottawa, 1932, the United Kingdom undertakes to continue duty-free admission to imports from the British Empire of goods subject to duty under the provisions of the Import Duties Act, 1932.

CANADA

The Canadian customs tariff specifically provides for the duty-free entry of sulphate of ammonia (item 208) and nitrate of soda (item 210). However, there are certain taxes to be taken into consideration, approximately 9 per cent of the value, with certain exceptions; namely, a special excise tax of 3 per cent which applies to practically all imported goods, but not to goods of Canadian manufacture or production; and a sales tax of 6 per cent which applies not only to imported goods but also to Canadian goods with certain exceptions. The 3 per cent tax does not apply to goods imported by mail or express if valued at not more than $25. The 6 per cent sales tax does not apply at the time of importation if the products are imported by licensed manufacturers.

APPENDIX VII

THE EFFECT OF THE SYNTHETIC NITROGEN INDUSTRY ON PRICES OF NITROGEN IN THE UNITED STATES.

NITROGEN PRICES

Sulphate of Ammonia

1919..............$97.50 per ton
1932 (domestic).... 22.00 per ton
1932 (imported).... 19.00 per ton—20% of 1919 price.

Nitrate of Soda

1919..............$88.50 per ton
1932.............. 35.40 per ton—39% of 1919 price.

Calcium Cyanamid

1919..............$88.50 per ton
1932.............. 26.00 per ton—29% of 1919 price.

WHOLESALE PRICES OF NITRATE OF SODA, SULPHATE OF AMMONIA, AND CALCIUM CYANAMID

(Dollars per unit of 20 pounds of nitrogen)

	Nitrate of Soda		Sulphate of Ammonia		Calcium Cyanamid	
	Price per Unit of N	Per cent of 1919 Price	Price per Unit of N	Per cent of 1919 Price	Price per Unit of N	Per cent of 1919 Price
January—						
1919..........	$5.71	100	$4.65	100	$4.02	100
1920..........	4.09	72	6.42	138	4.93	123
1921..........	3.65	64	3.25	70	2.94	73
1922..........	3.03	53	2.60	56	2.64	66
1923..........	3.35	59	3.36	72	2.67	66
1924..........	3.19	56	2.73	59	2.19	55
1925....:.....	3.37	59	2.96	64	2.01	50
1926..........	3.46	61	2.74	59	2.46	61
1927..........	3.38	59	2.43	52	2.25	56
1928..........	3.08	54	2.36	51	2.12	53
1929..........	2.85	50	2.26	49	2.31	58
1930..........	2.76	48	1.92	41	2.00	50
1931..........	2.62	46	1.45	31	1.70	42
1932..........	2.25	39	.97	21	1.18	29

From The Fertilizer Review, March, 1932.

APPENDIX VIII.

THE JAPANESE PRESS AND THE NITROGEN SITUATION

From the Kogyo Shimbun   January 23, 1932.

OVERSUPPLY OF SULPHATE OF AMMONIA TO BE EXPORTED

The estimated output of sulphate of ammonia in Japan for the first half of 1932, amounts to 407,500 tons, to which are added 100,000 tons of foreign sulphate of ammonia to be imported, making a total of over 500,000 tons. There being moreover an old stock brought over from 1931, the total prospective supply will exceed by far the demand. It will be necessary, therefore, for the Japanese factories to make curtailment of their estimated outputs in order to maintain the market, taking into consideration the amount of licenses to be given to foreign sulphate of ammonia. The future management has become a vital question to the Japanese producers.

The Mitsui and Mitsubishi firms, leading foreign sulphate of ammonia importers, in view of the excessive supply of sulphate of ammonia in Japan, are going to devote their energies to the exportation of the Japanese product. The chief destination intended is America. For the first half of 1931 the exports of sulphate of ammonia from various countries to America totalled 42,945 tons, of which 15,133 tons were from Canada, 9,411 tons from Belgium, 7,729 tons from Germany, 1,862 tons from Japan and 578 tons from France, as against 34,964 tons for the first half, 1930, increasing by about 10,000 tons. The American demand for sulphate of ammonia is expected to increase more and more, and the Mitsui and Mitsubishi firms intend supplying the comparatively cheap Japanese goods.

From the Osaka Asahi   June 22, 1932.

TALK OF CURTAILMENT OF PRODUCTION TO MEET
WORST SITUATION OF SULPHATE OF AMMONIA

EAST COMPANY OF SAME OPINION

The present market price is as low as ¥55.00 per ton, i.e., below the cost of production, and due to the poor demand for sulphate of ammonia overproduction is beginning to be felt. The Chisso Kyogikai (nitrogen conference) held a meeting at the Chuotei Restaurant, Marunouchi, on the 18th and consulted manufacturing companies about the following policies:

1. To curtail the output in proportion to the productive capacity of each company.
2. To consider what measures to take in order to make a clean sweep of foreign goods from the market.

Each company, in principle, supported the above policies, but as no decision was made it was decided to hold another conference.

———

From the Osaka Asahi   July 27, 1932.

TO GIVE UP DOMESTIC MARKET

AIMS AT MARKET ABROAD

Signs of a Turning Point for Japan's Nitrogen Industry as a Result of Europe's Convention on Nitrogen

The international nitrogen convention, already reported in these columns, has been established by European countries and they are now persuading Chile to join it. The establishment of this international nitrogen convention will have no direct effect on Japan's fertilizer industry as her foreign trade is under a license system, but European countries can now move together as one man and it will facilitate their negotiations with Japan. There are signs that, if deemed necessary or expedient, Japanese business men will enter into the following agreements with foreign countries in regard to those markets where Japanese goods are sold. At present the Chinese market requires about 200,000 tons per year, all of which are supplied by Britain and Germany, and Japan will export to China about 50,000 tons on condition that she does not extend her export trade with the South Sea Islands. For the Pacific coast of the United States of America, Japan will enter into an agreement with Holland who exports to that region, and open a new market in North America for Japanese goods. Should Japan cooperate with Holland to prevent dumping, she will be able to export to the Pacific coast of North America about 20,000 tons per year.

Anyway, the license system has lost its power, and while there is in Japan a very delicate relation between fertilizers and agricultural problems, we find abroad the revival of the international nitrogen convention. Thus, we see signs that Japan's fertilizer industry will face a turning point sooner or later.

INDEX